CANADIAN HEALTH INFORMATION

A PRACTICAL LEGAL AND RISK MANAGEMENT GUIDE

THIRD EDITION

LORNE ELKIN ROZOVSKY, Q.C., F.C.L.M. (hon.)
Member of the Nova Scotia Bar

and

NOELA JOY INIONS, BScN (hon.), LLM, CHE
Member of the Alberta and Northwest Territories Bars

LexisNexis®

Canadian Health Information
© Butterworths Canada Ltd. 2002
October 2002

Members of the LexisNexis Group worldwide

Canada	LexisNexis Canada Inc, 123 Commerce Valley Dr. E. Suite 700, MARKHAM, Ontario
Argentina	Abeledo Perrot, Jurisprudencia Argentina and Depalma, BUENOS AIRES
Australia	Butterworths, a Division of Reed International Books Australia Pry Ltd, CHATSWOOD, New South Wales
Austria	ARD Betriebsdienst and Verlag Orac, VIENNA
Chile	Publitecsa and Conosur Ltda, SANTIAGO DE CHILE
Czech Republic	Orac, sro, PRAGUE
France	Éditions du Juris-Classeur SA, PARIS
Hong Kong	Butterworths Asia (Hong Kong), HONG KONG
Hungary	Hvg Orac, BUDAPEST
India	Butterworths India, NEW DELHI
Ireland	Butterworths (Ireland) Ltd, DUBLIN
Italy	Giuffré, MILAN
Malaysia	Malayan Law Journal Sdn Bhd, KUALA LUMPUR
New Zealand	Butterworths of New Zealand, WELLINGTON
Poland	Wydawnictwa Prawnicze PWN, WARSAW
Singapore	Butterworths Asia, SINGAPORE
South Africa	Butterworth Publishers (Pty) Ltd, DURBAN
Switzerland	Stämpfli Verlag AG, BERNE
United Kingdom	Butterworths Tolley, a Division of Reed Elsevier (UK), LONDON, WC2A
USA	LexisNexis, DAYTON, Ohio

National Library of Canada Cataloguing in Publication

Rozovsky, Lorne Elkin, 1942-
  Canadian health information: a practical legal and risk management guide / Lorne Elkin Rozovsky, Noela Inions. — 3rd ed.

Includes index.
ISBN 978-0-433-42381-2

  1. Medical records — Law and legislation — Canada. I. Inions, Noela J. II. Title.

KE3646.R69 2002   344.71'041   C2002-904305-0

Printed and bound in Canada.

Reprint #2.

Foreword

Health information is the lifeblood of the health care system. That information, set out in health records, is critical to the diagnosis, care and treatment of the patient and is of significance to health care institutions, health care professionals and researchers. It may also be determinative of the accountability of care-givers and institutions. Because of the nature of the information, there are also privacy interests to be respected. In the last 10 years, significant changes have occurred in the way in which health information is collected, stored, used and disclosed.

This text is a most helpful statement and a reliable guide to anyone who works with or has an interest in health information. The topic is difficult to write about because policies, legislation and case law determine the requirements and standards and these can vary from province to province. This is especially so in recent times.

The strength of the text is that it deals with and describes basic principles and provides guidance for action where there is a void. The interpretation of statutory requirements can be very difficult, even for those who are part of the legal system, so that it is no surprise that it can be a daunting task for others. This text, and especially this edition, provides the reader with assistance. It also provides a clear description of the law flowing from decided cases.

It should be the goal of every lawyer author to describe the law, be it case law or statute law, in plain language. The authors succeed admirably. Given their backgrounds, this is not surprising. Both have spent considerable time working within health care as consultants, advisers and teachers. And, most importantly, both have a great deal of knowledge and experience in dealing with health information.

Lorne Rozovsky wrote the first book on hospital law in Canada. *Canadian Hospital Law: A Practical Guide* was published in 1974. Many of us remember it as a reliable, practical statement of the law. Lorne has written more extensively on health law than any other Canadian. He has had a career spanning 35 years in which he has been a practitioner, professor, counsel and consultant to national and international organizations and governments, author, editor and media person. His commitment to teaching health care workers and professionals about law has put him in touch will all the problems and concerns faced by those working with health information.

Noela Inions began her career as a nurse. She went on to a career in law, specializing in health law. She has been a practitioner, consultant to provincial and national organizations, author and an educator. She spent many years as in-house counsel for large hospitals and health regions where she was responsible for the legal and risk management areas. She has worked extensively with government seeking to achieve a balance between access and privacy in health information legislation and is now legal counsel on health information for the Alberta Information and Privacy Commissioner. She has 30 years of experience relevant to the topics in this book.

Put simply, these authors know what they are talking about. In this book they share that collective knowledge and experience with the reader.

The Honourable Madam Justice Ellen Picard
Alberta Court of Appeal,
Northwest Territories Supreme Court
and Northwest Territories Court of Appeal
June 26, 2002

How to Use this Book

THE PURPOSE OF THIS BOOK

Canadian Health Information is specifically written for health professionals, administrative staff, health planners and consultants, and their legal counsel. It is designed as a practical guide that is a quick and easy reference.

It is a succinct description of the legal issues affecting the practical day-to-day use of health information in health organizations. This edition takes into account that health information goes far beyond what have traditionally been referred to as "health records" or, in the past, "patient records". It recognizes that health information may be found in hospitals, long-term care facilities, clinics, the offices of solo physicians and other health practitioners, home care agencies, health associations and government agencies.

The focus of the book is on the prevention or, at least, minimization of the risks of lawsuits and other legal proceedings, and discusses both the legal implications and risk management techniques.

It provides advice to assist in identifying, avoiding or at least controlling potential legal problems. Hopefully it will provide assistance to the reader who is not a lawyer in discussing the issues with legal counsel. The advice is intended for those who are actively involved in the use of health information, as well as those whose responsibilities include the supervision of those who may be involved, and in setting or advising organizational policy and procedure.

The book should also assist lawyers in identifying the legal problems faced by those who work with health information, and provide some guidelines on the legal foundations involved. It should also be useful in assisting lawyers who advise health policy-makers.

The authors have attempted to provide a basic guide from a Canadian perspective based on Canadian law and practice.

Canadian Health Information is not designed to be an exhaustive discussion of legal principles or philosophy. Legal theories and comparisons of legal approaches used in legal decisions have been avoided. The book does not claim to be a complete or necessarily up-to-date statement of the status of the law. Regulations and statutes are constantly changing at the provincial, territorial and federal levels. The authors have made every attempt to ensure the accuracy of the law at the time the manuscript was completed. Legislative changes could very well occur, however, prior to publication and certainly after publication. As a result, the book identifies the legal issues and legislation which exists, and directs the reader to refer to that legislation.

No legal text, even one that is designed to be practically oriented, can be used in place of the advice of legal counsel. Legal advice is tailored to meet a specific situation in very specific circumstances. *Canadian Health Information* will alert the reader to those situations in which legal advice is required or at least advisable, and give the reader some assistance in the issues involved.

Lorne E. Rozovsky
Noela J. Inions

Acknowledgements

The authors extend their thanks to the following people who have been extremely supportive, encouraging and helpful in the research and writing of this book:

The Honourable Madam Justice E.I. Picard, Court of Appeal of Alberta; Elma G. Heidemann, Executive Director, Canadian Council on Health Services Accreditation; Gail Crook, Executive Director, Canadian Health Record Association; Kathryn Arbuckle, Law Librarian, Weir Law Library, University of Alberta; Michael Storozuk, Reference Librarian, Weir Law Library, University of Alberta; Brent Windwick, Executive Director, Health Law Institute, University of Alberta; Tim Caulfield, Research Director, Health Law Institute, University of Alberta; Nina Hawkins, Administrator, Health Law Institute, University of Alberta.

Research for this edition was conducted by the authors at the John A. Weir Memorial Law Library at the University of Alberta.

Table of Contents

Table of Cases

G

H

I

K

L

M

About the Authors

Lorne E. Rozovsky, Q.C., is the author of the first book ever published on Canadian Hospital Law. This is his seventeenth book. He is the author of over 600 articles on health law and has lectured in every province and territory in Canada, as well as in the United States, Europe, Africa, the West Indies and Israel. He has served as a consultant to health organizations, government agencies and corporations, and for a number of years served on the faculties of law, medicine and dentistry at Dalhousie University in Halifax, N.S. In 1986 he was appointed as the only Canadian an honorary fellow of the American College of Legal Medicine and prior to that was the only Canadian to be invited to appear as an expert witness before the Secretary's Commission on Medical Malpractice in the U.S.

Noela J. Inions, is a professor with Central Michigan University and Associate Professor of the Faculty of Nursing at the University of Alberta. She has presented on medico-legal topics extensively in Alberta, as well as across Canada, in Australia, the United States and Europe. She has practised as a registered nurse in Alberta and the United States. She is a health law practitioner and has served as a member and on the board of Directors for various national and provincial health and health law organizations. She has been a consultant to Alberta Health and Wellness and in-house counsel for many years on clinical legal issues to various hospitals and the Capital Health Authority Region. Since 1999, Noela has been legal counsel to the Information and Privacy Commissioner of Alberta.

Other Books by the Authors

Lorne E. Rozovsky

Canadian Hospital Law: A Practical Guide (also in French as Le droit hospitalier au Canada: guide pratique)

Canadian Manual on Hospital By-laws (with W.M. Dunlop)

Canadian Hospital Law, 2nd Edition

The Canadian Patient's Book of Rights

Canadian Dental Law

The Canadian Patient's Book of Rights (revised and updated)

The Canadian Law of Consent to Treatment, 2nd Edition

L.E. and F.A. Rozovsky

Legal Sex

Canadian Health Facilities Law Guide

Canadian Law of Patient Records

Canadian Health Facilities Law Guide

Canadian Law of Consent to Treatment

Canadian Health Information: A Legal and Risk Management Guide, 2nd Edition

AIDS and Canadian Law

Home Health Care Law: Liability and Risk Management (USA)

Medical Staff Credentialing: A Practical Guide (with L. Harpster) (USA)

Noela J. Inions

Privilege and Quality Assurance: The Issues for Canadian Hospitals

1

Health Information and the Law

WHAT IS HEALTH INFORMATION?

With the explosion in the amount of and access to information in the health system, old terminology sounds very much out of date. Traditionally, the information about the condition and treatment of patients was referred to as "medical records". The use of this term was uniform whether the records were found in a hospital, a nursing home, an outpatient clinic or a physician's office.

The term "medical" was applied even though not all the information recorded emanated from the care or treatment given by physicians. Included in the records were nurses' notes, reports from laboratories of tests done by technologists, consultations from psychologists, social workers and physiotherapists and x-ray and other diagnostic findings.

The records were "medical" however, in the sense that they were used by physicians to determine the diagnosis and course of treatment. While individuals from other disciplines had access to the records and based their own judgments on the information, the ultimate decisions were made by physicians. By and large this has not changed.

With the increasing sophistication of information systems and emphasis on illness prevention and health promotion, the term "medical records" has become too restrictive. It implies information gathered and used in acute care settings such as hospitals. However, health information is also collected at well-baby clinics, industrial plants, schools and prisons. Information collected in tertiary care is transferred to primary care settings and vice versa. The term also overlooks the growing emphasis on employee health, public health organizations, psychiatric clinics, home health programs, lodges, assisted living and private health facilities.

As a result the term "health records" came into vogue. The Canadian Medical Record Association became the Canadian Health Record Association (CHRA). The medical record librarian became the health record administrator. With advances in technology the written record is now only one method of documenting information about the individual and the health services provided. The more common term now is "health information", with the patient more often being referred to as the client or individual. Despite this trend terms such as "patient record", "medical record" and "health record" are still used.

In some jurisdictions the terminology has been imposed on certain sectors of the health system by provincial legislation. Legislation may from time to time be inconsistent as between statutes and regulations and common usage. Great care must be taken to instruct staff that legislative references to health information or to a record by a particular title may in fact refer to information commonly known by another name. Definitions and references may vary between and even within health facilities. Much depends on who is using the information and for what purpose.

Regardless of whether there is a statutory or regulatory definition or designation, particular care must be taken in legal proceedings, in dealings with lawyers and insurance companies and in any communication with respect to health information. With such a variety of terms used to describe information maintained about an individual's health, it is important that communications clearly designate what information is meant.

It may be useful to use an all-inclusive reference such as "and all other information". Failure to be clear about the information needed may result in communication errors. Records may not be brought to the attention of the person requesting them, thus affecting settlement negotiations and court proceedings.

Because health information exists under widely divergent circumstances, this book uses the term "health information". This term refers to all types of information pertaining to the health of an individual under treatment or care regardless of where it was collected, used or disclosed, unless specific reference is made to a particular type of record. This term includes pre-hospital notations made by emergency medical attendants, physiotherapy and chiropractic notes, occupational health files, consultations and diagnostic reports. Health information includes information supplied by the patient on hospital cards, Smart Cards, Medic Alert bracelets, durable power of attorney forms and living wills.

Health information includes information contained on CD ROMs, faxes, e-mail, computers and digital recordings. Health information can be communicated by any type of electronic means such as by the Internet or by telehealth or e-health. The principles discussed, with a few exceptions, are directed at all health information regardless of department, service, patient, personnel or health care situation.

WHAT IS THE LAW?

As in any subject, the law is not found in one place. There are now a few health information acts at the provincial level. Personal information is governed by freedom of information and protection of privacy (FOIP) legislation in the public sector and by the *Personal Information Protection and Electronic Documents Act (PIPEDA)*[1] in the private sector. Principles that relate to health information are scattered throughout dozens of enactments and court decisions.

Health information legislation is found within broader legislation governing different types of health facilities, health services and providers of service. Reference must be made to provincial enactments for hospitals, regional health authorities, ambulance services, mental health, cancer programs, nursing homes, public health, occupational health and safety, organ donation, health professions, health insurance plans and so on.

A particular set of records will not be governed only by legislation directed solely at a particular health service provider. Legislation directed at particular circumstances will also govern. For example, health information related to communicable disease in a hospital record may be regulated by the hospital act of that province, the by-laws of the hospital and the public health act. The information may also be affected by provincial legislation that requires reporting for purposes of vital statistics, fatality inquiries or adult abuse.

When the information is used in court, federal or provincial rules of court and evidence acts are applied. To a certain extent, the law of health information is found in common law decisions or judge-made law. Certain questions such as access to health information have been dealt with from time to time by the courts. However, most legal questions concerning health information have not been addressed by the courts.

Judges occasionally comment on matters involving the health information or the records, but these remarks are often not binding precedent. One must speculate as to how the legal outcome might have been different if the situation were altered. With regard to health information in court, reference should be made to the appropriate rules of court.

As Canadians are less litigious and Canada is a smaller country than American, there are fewer Canadian court decisions. Many of the legal questions which arise in the United States have been considered by the courts of that country. This is not so in Canada where the answers remain speculative. United States government agencies, both at the federal and state levels, promulgate regulations to a far greater extent than their Canadian counterparts.

---

[1] S.C. 2000, c. 5.

Answers to questions regarding health information are often found in legislation in that country, whereas Canadian law is silent. The result is that the practice of compiling health information is largely left in the hands of those who are gathering it, although there are now a number of legislative enactments in Canada.

HEALTH INFORMATION AND THE LAWYER

Ordinarily, lawyers are the last group to become involved in health information issues unless legal action is threatened. Lawyers are often retained to respond only after a crisis occurs. However, it is unwise to limit the role of legal counsel to these situations.

Health information, in addition to whatever else it may be, includes legal documents. Health information is used for "legal" purposes and carries with it legal consequences as a result of other uses. (See Chapter 2 — Purposes of Health Information). In the practice of "preventive law", to avoid potential legal problems, legal counsel should be involved in the planning and review of any health information system. When potential problems are identified, approaches can be devised to address them. In this way the health information system can become an integral part of a liability risk management program.

In particular, legal counsel should be involved in the following:

1. review and interpretation of common law decisions, statutes, regulations, by-laws and orders that affect health information practices;
2. review of contracts and other arrangements, which may have a legal effect on health information practices;
3. implementation of changes to health information systems that may impact confidentiality, privacy or security, particularly when the change involves electronic means;
4. policies, procedures and forms for documenting health services provided and situations involving improper documentation such as defamatory comments;
5. policies, procedures and processes for individuals requesting to access, amend or correct their health information;
6. policies, procedures and processes for the collection, use and disclosure of health information particularly disclosure to third parties and transborder data flows;
7. policies, procedures, forms and agreements for using health information for secondary purposes such as education and research;

8. policies, procedures, forms and practices for using health information for internal management and quality improvement activities such as incident reporting, legal advice pending litigation, utilization review, practice review and performance appraisal;

9. policies, procedures and forms for documenting individual decisions such as consent and refusal of care;

10. policies, procedures and processes for the retention, storage and disposal of health information including microfilming procedures; and

11. policies, procedures and processes for data matching, data linkage and re-identification activities.

Regular legal reviews of health information systems will minimize the likelihood of legal problems arising later on. It is important that legal advice is disseminated to all persons involved in health information activities.

2

Purposes of Health Information

OVERVIEW

The questions asked of lawyers about health information are numerous. How long must information be kept? Can documents be microfilmed? Can they be computerized? What is permanent and has to be included? What is temporary and can be left out? How are errors corrected? Who can see the information? Does the patient have the right of access? Should the information be transferred from one facility to another? Can the information be used as the basis for a lawsuit?

Few of these questions can be answered without asking a preliminary question: what is the purpose of the information? Why is this information collected? How is the information used, disclosed, destroyed and retained? The question does not apply to health information in general but to specific records. The answer to the question may differ with respect to different patients being treated by the same physician, health service or health facility. The answer may even differ with respect to different parts of the health information of any one patient.

The purpose of the information cannot be fully described by any one individual. Those who are knowledgeable in its use must be sought out. Information in a hospital setting might involve medical, nursing, administrative and dietetic services. The advice of social workers, physiotherapists and psychologists may be required in community health care settings. Statisticians, auditors and legal counsel may be called upon, as well as accrediting, licensing and funding bodies.

Many of the purposes for collecting or maintaining health information may be found in the following list, which is not in any particular order or priority:

1. *Clinical.* The main reason for collecting and maintaining health information is to enable health personnel to provide treatment and care for the patient. Health information enables judgments to be made, such as diagnoses and prognoses. The clinical basis for documentation falls within the duty to provide average, reasonable and prudent care.

Care may involve numerous settings such as ambulances, hospitals, home care, public health and nursing homes, and various care providers such as medical, nursing and dental personnel. Documentation communicates the care already given and the condition of the patient among caregivers.

Communication is particularly important in large facilities where many people are caring for the patient without any direct personal contact with each other. Nurses on different shifts must coordinate their care and know what others have done. Communication must take place between nurses directly in contact with the patient on a daily basis and staff of various diagnostic, dietary, pharmaceutical and medical services. The failure to record information or to record it correctly, can result in inappropriate care and patient injury.

While inherent risks and errors in judgment may not in themselves be considered as acts of negligence, errors with respect to records are more likely to be considered negligent. The question is: should the provider know or ought to have known of the foreseeable injury as a result of making such an error? If the court answers the question in the affirmative, this could be the basis for a finding of negligence since the record keeping was not performed in a reasonable and prudent manner.

The situations in which such a finding could result are obvious. Negligence suits are often settled out of court and many errors do not result in legal action. However, the failure to record, communicate or act on information is a possible basis for a finding of negligence. Health information may describe allergies or sensitivities, which increase the risk of treatment or care. Risks may involve drugs or diet.

The patient may not be aware or may be unable to communicate risks and therefore should not always be expected to volunteer information with respect to allergies or sensitivities. Because of the high risk of injury with allergies, a procedure should be established to immediately draw allergies to the attention of everyone treating the patient. This applies equally to private medical, dental, physiotherapy, optometric or chiropractic practice, community health care and public facility settings.

2.   *Cultural and Religious Services.* As religious affiliation with health facilities diminishes and the complexity of care increases, there appears to be a growing need for multicultural, ethnic and pastoral services. There is increased sensitivity to needs of ethnic, cultural and religious minorities and their feelings about religious matters. Information may be collected regarding ethnic or religious affiliation to provide patients with pastoral services and to make accommodation for cultural needs. To this extent, the religious purpose is related to or an adjunct of the clinical purpose.

From a legal point of view, great care must be taken not to infringe provincial human rights or privacy legislation. In any facility that is ordinarily open to the public, no discrimination may take place with respect to an individual's ethnic group or religion. It is essential that the collection and recording of ethnic or religious information be related to services sought by the individual. Accusations could be made either that discrimination or preference in accommodation or service occurred as a result of this information. The procedure for obtaining this type of information and use and disclosure should be reviewed by legal counsel.

3.　*Educational.* Many health agencies function as educational facilities as well as health providers. The teaching function may involve bringing outside students into the facility, running in-house teaching programs or operating continuing education programs for facility staff.

The educational function may involve medical students, interns and residents, bioethics residents, dental, nursing, health records, administrative and pastoral students as well as students in any of the health technologies. Programs are usually approved or accredited by some external body. Approval may be given by a governmental agency, by a university or other external educational institution or by a professional or disciplinary board, college or association.

The approval is given based on particular criteria. One of the criteria will likely be the standard of care in the facility. The standard of care is measured to a large extent by review of health records and by using health information as a teaching tool. If the record keeping in the facility falls below the standard acceptable to the appropriate approving or accrediting body, the facility may not be permitted to train students or may fail to attract students.

This may require the replacement of student manpower with paid employees and may also result in loss of funding. Reputation may be affected so that it is more difficult to recruit and retain high quality staff. The consequences of poor records can be serious.

4.　*Research.* Health information is used for research projects by facilities and individual practitioners. Research may involve the cause and course of illness, the effects of treatment, the condition of patients regardless of treatment or the effects of non-therapeutic intervention conducted solely for scientific advancement. Poor records jeopardize the validity of the research.

The legal implications of health information kept for research purposes are twofold. The first implication is the research project itself. Since the quality of the records may affect the quality of the research and the accuracy of the results, poor or incomplete records may jeopardize funding for the project. The funding agency may have a contract with the researcher that includes qualitative and quantitative criteria. Failure to meet these criteria may amount to breach of contract with the funding agency and the withdrawal of funding, resources and benefits.

The second implication relates to research involving bodily intervention. The same problems arise as with health information maintained for clinical purposes. The failure to maintain quality records may result in patient or resident injury that could amount to negligence.

If research involves intervention of an experimental nature, regardless of whether it is therapeutic, the law requires above average care.[1] If health information could affect the quality of care, research records should be compiled to minimize not only reasonably foreseeable injuries but also more remote injuries. Research is discussed in more detail in Chapter 16 — Human Research and Health Information.

5.   *Risk and Quality Management.* Health information is used for a wide range of risk, quality and utilization management activities. Health information is used for compiling risk and quality analyses, which may indicate a falling quality of care in a rising incidence of neo-natal death or post-operative infection. Statistical and case-by-case analyses provide the basis for evaluation of successes or deficiencies in programs such as trauma, transplantation, kidney dialysis and intensive care.

The failure to conduct meaningful follow-up may be viewed as negligence, when evaluating, monitoring and auditing would have identified problems and enabled action to minimize injury. One of the recommendations that was made by the Dubin Inquiry following the pediatric cardiac deaths at the Toronto Hospital for Sick Children, was that facilities should have rigorous monitoring programs to enable early intervention.

Health information is used by numerous accrediting agencies for accrediting health services. For example, the Canadian Council on Health Services Accreditation (CCHSA) operates a voluntary accreditation program for facilities such as hospitals, mental health centres, community health services and extended care facilities. The survey team inspects the facility using various goals, objectives and guides as the basis of the assessment.

Standards described in by-laws, mission statements, goals, objectives, policies and procedures are reviewed. The accreditation report provided to health facilities includes commendations as well as areas of deficiency. Specific deficiencies described in accreditation reports can be powerful evidence in the hands of a plaintiff's lawyer or the media. Deficiencies in health information standards that result in foreseeable injury make a strong case for negligence. Risk and quality management is discussed in more detail in Chapter 17 — Risk Management in Health Information.

6.   *Peer Review and Professional Discipline.* Health information is essential for conducting performance appraisals and continuing competence activities for health professionals. In specific incidents, health information may be the basis for staff discipline. As a result of a complaint, a particular incident, or an audit, an individual may come under investi-

---

[1]   *Halushka v. University of Saskatchewan* (1965), 52 W.W.R. 608, 53 D.L.R. (2d) 436 (Sask. C.A.). See also *Weiss c. Solomon* (1989), 48 C.C.L.T. 280 (Que. S.C.).

gation and review by a hospital committee and subsequently by the board of management or trustees. These steps may result in the restriction or removal of a physician's, dentist's or midwife's privileges to admit or treat patients. Health information is usually a vital tool in the process.

Professional regulatory bodies are responsible to protect the public by licensing and registering members of health professions and health disciplines. These bodies are charged with investigating complaints, examining evidence and holding hearings. Decisions are made about whether the member is guilty of unprofessional conduct and is reprimanded or suspended. Health information is essential for conducting such proceedings.

The question arises as to whether patients could prevent health information from being used for peer review or professional disciplinary proceedings. If the patient is also the complainant, consent can be readily obtained. In other situations, statutory exceptions authorize disclosure and require privacy protection without the need to obtain patient consent.

7. *Management, Audit and Inspection.* One of the most important reasons for maintaining health information is for management purposes. Health facilities, agencies and providers require management to provide health services. Examples of management functions include assessment, evaluation, reporting, planning and resource allocation such as staffing units, opening beds and closing programs. Administration of local, regional, provincial and national health services as well as the coordination and integration of services requires health information. In addition, policy development, health reform and restructuring also depend upon health information.

Audit and inspection are necessary to ensure that a particular quality of service has been achieved. Apart from comments and opinions of those involved in a particular case, the audit or inspection of individual cases depends mainly on health information. The audit of medical care is carried out by committees of the medical staff and the audit of nursing care is often carried out by designated staff. Similarly, care and treatment given by other disciplines is subject to audit and inspection activities.

Audit and evaluation is not restricted to the review of care and treatment of a particular patient, but examines the pattern of care and treatment provided to many patients. This may be the only way that errors or accidents are discovered to enable action to be taken to prevent reoccurrence in the future. Failure to take such action could amount to negligence.

Many facilities require provincial government licences to operate.[2] Nursing homes and hospitals are subject to government inspections from time to time. While there may be statutory or regulatory requirements for particular information to be maintained, many of the requirements with respect to record keeping may be based either on government policy or on the opinion of an operator. Therefore, a further purpose in maintaining health information is to obtain and maintain a licence to operate.

8. *Insurance and Financial.* Most health services in Canada are insured under provincial health insurance plans. Health services are funded by a variety of provincial and municipal government programs, such as children's and senior's programs, ambulance services, public health clinics and mental health centres. Examples of funding agencies include provincial Medicare, Veterans Affairs, Indian Affairs and Northern Development, Corrections Canada and provincial worker's compensation regimes. Partial or complete coverage for health services may exist under private insurance carriers or services may be paid for by the individual.

Health information is used to determine eligibility for health services, responsibility for payment, and for processing and seeking payment. Health information may be disclosed for purposes of third party payment. Health information is essential for adjudication and audit of benefit and insurance claims for coverages related to health services, disability and deaths. Health information may be used for marketing services such as selling insurance coverage.

Funding requirements for health facilities and health insurance programs may be found in legislation that compels facilities and health providers to maintain particular records. In other instances the form of record keeping is prescribed by policy directives or by mutual agreements, for example electronic claims. Failure to maintain and report the required information may jeopardize not only promptness but payment.

Apart from any specific direction from funding agencies, records need to be maintained to support claims for payment. A physician may need to prove that patients were treated and provided with the services that were billed. Health information is used to determine whether a physician has been overtreating a patient to increase claims.

The same principles apply to other service providers billing under public or private insurance plans such as dentists, chiropractors and physiotherapists. Under health or hospital insurance plans, only medically necessary treatment is insured,[3] so a hospital may be required to

---

[2] See *e.g.*, *Nursing Homes Act*, R.S.O. 1990, c. N.7, s. 4.

[3] See *e.g.*, *Health Insurance Act*, R.S.O. 1990, c. H.6, s. 11.2(2); *Saskatchewan Medical Care Insurance Act*, R.S.S. 1978, c. S-29, s. 14(1).

justify the presence of a patient in the hospital. Health information is used to support such arguments.

Another purpose for maintaining health information exists for health providers who pay income tax. This includes physicians, dentists, optometrists, podiatrists, accupuncturists, chiropractors, physiotherapists and pharmacists in private practice as well as operators of nursing homes, ambulance services and medical clinics. Revenue Canada has the authority to demand supporting documentation for deductions and business expenses,[4] which may be found in health records.

9. *Legal Proceedings.* Another way that health information is used is for a variety of legal proceedings such as beneficiaries challenging wills, families seeking custody or guardianship, personal injury litigation, administrative tribunals such as hospital privileges appeal boards and criminal proceedings. Health facilities are served with a wide variety of court and statutory orders such as search warrants, subpoenas and Notices to Attend or Produce that compel disclosure of health information.

Health information is used for defence of litigation against health facilities and providers. Litigation arising in the health setting includes actions for negligence, assault and battery, breach of contract, breach of confidentiality, false imprisonment, defamation and quasi-criminal proceedings for breach of various statutory obligations. It may not be possible to remember details or a particular incident years later when a lawsuit is commenced. Health information therefore forms the primary line of defence.

At one time this was not possible as introducing health records in legal proceedings was contrary to the hearsay rule.[5] This rule prohibited the introduction into evidence of statements made by people other than the witnesses.[6] Under evidence legislation throughout Canada and in the Supreme Court of Canada decision in *Ares v. Venner,*[7] health records are now permitted into evidence as *prima facie* proof of the facts stated in them.

The recording of health information, therefore, is a collection of evidence that may defend care providers. Alternatively, if the care was substandard, the health information will be evidence against health facilities and health care providers. (For further discussion, see Chapter 6 — Health Information as Evidence.)

10. *Legislative.* Another reason for maintaining health information is compliance with legislative requirements that are specified in various

---

[4] *Income Tax Act*, R.S.C. 1985, c. 1 (5th Supp.), ss. 231-231.6.

[5] E.I. Picard & G. Robertson, *Legal Liability of Doctors and Hospitals in Canada,* 3rd ed. (Toronto: Carswell, 1996), at 299-300.

[6] *Ibid.*

[7] [1970] S.C.R. 608, 73 W.W.R. 347, 14 D.L.R. (3d) 4, at 16, 12 C.R.N.S. 349.

statutes and regulations. Legislation that requires records to be maintained may also specify the required content and the method of maintenance. These provisions are ordinarily found in provincial statutes or regulations governing a particular category of facility such as a hospital or a long term care facility. Failure to abide by these provisions could result in prosecution, loss of funding, loss of licence or sanctions for breach of the legislation.

A legislative requirement at the federal level is the *Narcotic Control Regulations* that require physicians, dentists, veterinarians, pharmacists and others who deal in narcotics to keep records and make returns.[8] Failure to follow such regulations can result in prosecution or loss of permission to deal in narcotics. The regulations under the federal *Food and Drugs Act* have similar provisions.[9]

Specific records are required under the *Criminal Code* of Canada[10] and provincial mental health legislation[11] for various purposes including assessments of an accused to determine fitness to stand trial and for advising review boards. Most legislative requirements that apply to health information exist at the provincial and territorial level.

Health sector legislation may not only establish documentation requirements but may also prescribe how health information may be accessed by the individual and may establish detailed rules for collecting, using, disclosing, retaining and destroying health information. Legislation may require reporting for numerous reasons such as unexpected death, communicable disease, child and elder abuse, unsafe drivers and pilots, workers' compensation and vital statistics. (For more detailed discussions, see Chapter 5 — Retention, Storage and Disposal; Chapter 7 — Access to Health Information, and Chapter 8 — Confidentiality, Privacy and Disclosure to Third Parties).

PRACTICAL CONSIDERATIONS

1. *Identify Key Purposes* — Each health facility, health agency and health provider has somewhat different purposes for health information. It is essential that key purposes of health information be identified for each care setting.

---

[8] C.R.C. 1978, c. 1041, ss. 15, 41, 54, as am. by SOR/85-588, ss. 8, 14, 15, 12.

[9] C.R.C. 1978, c. 870, ss. G.03.008, G.04.002, as am. by SOR/97-228, ss. 10, 12, 14, 18.

[10] R.S.C. 1985, c. C-46, s. 672.11.

[11] See *e.g.*, *Mental Health Act*, S.P.E.I. 1994, c. 39, s. 27; *The Housing and Special Care Homes Act*, R.S.S. 1978, c. H-13, s. 18; *Hospitals Act*, R.S.N.S. 1989, c. 208, ss. 63-65; Ontario has established the Consent and Capacity Board under the *Health Care Consent Act, 1996*, S.O. 1996, c. 2, s. 50.

2. *Selectively Gather Health Information* — Health information should be collected only for the purposes identified. Once health information is gathered, many other obligations arise such as duties to provide individual access and to make appropriate use and disclosure of health information.

3. *Retention* — The key purposes of health information for your setting should be a key consideration when making other decisions such as retention, storage and disposal.

3

What Is Health Information?

OVERVIEW

Under constant debate is the question: what constitutes health information? What constitutes the health record? Does it include nurses' notes, laboratory reports, social work consultations and physicians' orders? Are x-rays, fluoroscopy images or tape recordings of magnetic resonance imaging (MRIs) included? What about the dietary Kardex? Are the notes of discharge planners and the pre-hospital notations from emergency medical attendants (EMAs) included?

What about Smartcards and other treatment information supplied by patients? What about the information involved in telehealth services, videoconferencing, palm pilots, faxes, laptops and computers? Are student's or researcher's notations included? Should nurses' aides make entries or should they report to nurses who will make the entries? The answers are not consistent. What one authority regards as health information or part of the health record is different from another. Therefore, the question is often posed to lawyers. There is no definite legal answer for all circumstances.

If there is a legal answer, it relates to the purposes for which the health information is used. The answer also depends upon administrative practice and how each health service categorizes its information including the label placed on each category. The question of whether consultations or nurses' notes or x-rays should be part of the record has no definite legal answer that is applicable to all circumstances.

In answering the question one must consider the purposes of health information, which were previously discussed in Chapter 2 — Purposes of Health Information. For example, health information must be collected in order to fulfill teaching, research or audit purposes. Ordinarily only those who are involved with the carrying out of those purposes need be consulted. If, however, external accrediting or professional bodies set standards for these activities, those standards must be considered. Various standards will be more fully discussed in Chapter 4 — Standards for Health Information.

If a contract or arrangement has been entered into between the facility such as a hospital and a funding agency including a provincial insurance plan, or a home care company and a government referral agency, legal advice should be sought. A determination must be made whether the arrangement imposes requirements regarding what health information is or is not to be collected and what form the documentation must take.

The information may be collected for more than one purpose. In such a case the requirements, both legal and otherwise, may emanate from different sources. Requirements set down for one reason should be considered as a minimum with further requirements being added to fulfill the other purposes. It can therefore be misleading to follow the requirements of a particular statute or regulation as the only requirements, without referring to additional criteria for maintaining health information.

The question of conflicting purposes must also be raised. Despite the primary importance of clinical purposes, any mandatory legislative requirements must be fulfilled to avoid legal sanctions such as a conviction. Directives with respect to government and health insurance plans must be complied with or payment might be denied. Conflicts between legislative enactments require the advice of legal counsel.

Definitions and requirements for the content of health information may be found in legislation. Most criteria for what health information must be recorded are flexible as to what should or should not be included. Discretion is permitted as long as the purpose is fulfilled. This is not the case with legislative requirements.

If federal or provincial legislation, whether in the form of statute or regulation, requires certain information to be recorded, there is no discretion. The only type of excuse that is acceptable for not complying with such a legislative directive is if the information is not available or cannot be collected.

FEDERAL LEGISLATION

Federal legislation now exists that defines health information in the private sector in Canada. The *Personal Information Protection and Electronic Documents Act* (*PIPEDA*),[1] for example, defines health information as follows:

> 2(1) "personal health information", with respect to an individual, whether living or deceased, means
> (a) information concerning the physical or mental health of the individual;

---

[1] S.C. 2000, c. 5, Part I, in force in part on January 1, 2001, January 1, 2002 and January 1, 2004.

(b)   information concerning any health service provided to the individual;

(c)   information concerning the donation by the individual of any body part or any bodily substance of the individual or information derived from the testing or examination of a body part or bodily substance of the individual;

(d)   information that is collected in the course of providing health services to the individual; or

(e)   information that is collected incidentally to the provision of health services to the individual.[2]

The *PIPEDA* definition of personal health information is unique as this definition is not limited to recorded information. This definition includes tissues and body fluids such as blood and urine samples and biometric information such as DNA sequences, fingerprints, blood type, and retinal patterns as well as the body substances from which the biometric information was obtained.

Other examples of federal legislation that affect requirements for health information are the *Controlled Drugs and Substances Act*,[3] the *Food and Drugs Act*[4] and the *Income Tax Act*.[5] Regulations such as the *Narcotic Control Regulations*[6] fall under *the Controlled Drugs and Substances Act*. The *Food and Drug Regulations*[7] that govern blood, semen and medical devices fall under the *Food and Drugs Act*.

The *Controlled Drugs and Substances Act* authorizes the Governor-in-Council to make regulations requiring physicians, dentists, veterinarians, pharmacists and other persons who deal in controlled drugs to keep records and make returns.[8] The *Narcotic Control Regulations* set out requirements for the information that must be documented by licensed dealers,[9] pharmacists,[10] medical practitioners[11] (including veterinarians) and hospitals.[12]

These requirements apply to any drug classified as a "controlled substance" that is included in the schedule to the *Controlled Drugs and Substances Act*. Controlled substances that are listed in the schedule include

---

[2]   *Ibid.*, s. 2(1). Note: This definition is now academic, as *PIPEDA* covers all types of personal information, including health information.

[3]   S.C. 1996, c. 19.

[4]   R.S.C. 1985, c. F-27.

[5]   R.S.C. 1985, c. 1 (5th Supp).

[6]   C.R.C. 1978, c. 1041.

[7]   C.R.C. 1978, c. 870.

[8]   *Supra*, n. 3, s. 20.

[9]   *Supra*, n. 6, s. 15.

[10]   *Ibid.*, ss. 30 and 38.

[11]   *Ibid.*, s. 54.

[12]   *Ibid.*, s. 63.

opium poppy, cannabis sativa, morphinans and benzazocines.[13] Specific
reference to the schedule must be made for the substances included and
excluded.

The provisions that apply to hospitals in the *Narcotic Control Regulations* specify that there must be a record of the dispensing of narcotics as follows:

> 63. A person who is in charge of a hospital shall
> (a) keep or cause to be kept in a book, register or other record maintained for such purposes,
>> (i)   the name and quantity of any narcotic received,
>> (ii)   the name and address of the person from whom any narcotic was received and the date received,
>> (iii) the name and quantity of any narcotic used in manufacturing,
>> (iv)   the name and quantity of any narcotic manufactured and the date of manufacture,
>> (v)   the name of the patient for whom a narcotic other than dextropropoxyphene or a verbal prescription narcotic was dispensed,
>> (vi)   the name of the practitioner ordering or prescribing a narcotic other than dextropropoxyphene or a verbal prescription narcotic, and
>> (vii) the date a narcotic other than dextropropoxyphene or a verbal prescription narcotic was ordered or prescribed and the form and quantity thereof;
> (b) maintain the recorded information in such form as to enable an audit to be made from time to time for a period of not less than two years from the making thereof;
> (c) take all necessary steps to protect narcotics in the hospital against loss or theft, and report to the Minister any loss or theft of narcotics within 10 days of his discovery thereof.[14]

The requirements differ depending on whether the drug is being handled by an institution, a licensed dealer, a pharmacist or a medical or veterinary practitioner.

The requirements for a controlled drug specify the type of information and how the records are to be kept. For example, drug records are to be kept separate from all other records. The *Narcotic Control Regulations* require hospitals to keep controlled drug information "in a book, register or similar record maintained exclusively for controlled drugs".[15] Similar provisions are found throughout the regulations directed at other entities and categories of drugs.

---

[13] *Supra*, n. 3, Schedule.
[14] *Supra*, n. 6, s. 63.
[15] *Ibid.*, s. G.05.001.

Therefore, records with respect to controlled drugs should be:

(a) maintained separately from each other;
(b) maintained separately from other health information;
(c) compiled according to the provisions of the appropriate federal act and regulations regardless of whether the information is required for any other purpose or not; and
(d) maintained in a separate record even though some of the information may be duplicated in records elsewhere for other purposes.

The *Food and Drugs Act* authorizes the Governor-in-Council to make regulations requiring persons who sell food, drugs, cosmetics or medical devices or provide blood or semen to maintain certain books and records as the Governor-in-Council considers necessary.[16] The regulations are similar to those made under the *Controlled Drugs and Substances Act* and require certain information to be recorded and maintained.

The *Income Tax Act*,[17] affects health facilities and personnel involved in private practice such as physicians, dentists and psychologists.[18] Under this Act, records must be kept according to directives put out by Revenue Canada in order to justify the claims made on tax returns. Since these directives may change annually, it is advisable to consult with Revenue Canada to determine the specific information required.

PROVINCIAL LEGISLATION

Statutes and regulations made at the provincial level establish requirements as to what health information must be recorded. The legislation is ordinarily directed at health facilities under the authority of general acts dealing with a particular category of facility, such as public hospitals or nursing homes.

The provinces of Manitoba, Alberta and Saskatchewan have now enacted public sector health information legislation that provides specific definitions for health information and health records.[19] Saskatchewan has not yet proclaimed its statute. This type of legislation creates the right of

---

[16] *Supra*, n. 4, s. 30.
[17] *Supra*, n. 5.
[18] *Ibid.*, ss. 231-231.6.
[19] *The Personal Health Information Act*, S.M. 1997, c. 51 (C.C.S.M. c. P33.5), assented to June 1997, proclaimed in force on December 11, 1997; *The Health Information Protection Act*, S.S. 1999, c. H-0.021, assented to May 1999, not yet proclaimed); *Health Information Act*, R.S.A. 2000, c. H-5, proclaimed in force April 25, 2001.

access by individuals to their own health information and protects the privacy of health information. Ontario has recently issued a draft combination Act[20] that would include public sector health information as well as private sector personal information.

The Alberta *Health Information Act*[21] contains a broad definition for health information. This definition includes diagnostic, treatment and care information, registration information and health services provider information.[22]

"Diagnostic, treatment and care information" is defined in the Alberta Act as:

1(1)(i) "diagnostic, treatment and care information" means information about any of the following:

(i) the physical and mental health of an individual;
(ii) a health service provided to an individual;
(iii) the donation by an individual of a body part or bodily substance, including information derived from the testing or examination of a body part or bodily substance;
(iv) a drug as defined in the Pharmaceutical Profession Act provided to an individual;
(v) a health care aid, device, product, equipment or other item provided to an individual pursuant to a prescription or other authorization;
(vi) the amount of any benefit paid or payable under the Alberta Health Care Insurance Act or any other amount paid or payable in respect of a health service provided to an individual,

and includes any other information about an individual that is collected when a health service is provided to the individual but does not include information that is not written, photographed, recorded or stored in some manner in a record; [23]

"Registration information" is defined in the Alberta Act as:

1(1)(u) "registration information" means information relating to an individual that falls within the following general categories and is more specifically described in the regulations:

(i) demographic information, including the individual's personal health number;
(ii) location information;
(iii) telecommunications information;
(iv) residency information;

---

[20] A Consultation on the Draft *Privacy of Personal Information Act, 2002*, Ontario, issued January 2002.
[21] R.S.A. 2000, c. H-5.
[22] *Ibid.*, s. 1(1)(k).
[23] *Ibid.*, s. 1(1)(i).

(v) health service eligibility information;

(vi) billing information,

but does not include information that is not written, photographed, recorded or stored in some manner in a record;[24]

The *Health Information Regulation*[25] provides a much more detailed description of registration information.

A "record" is defined in the Alberta Act as:

(t) "record" means a record of health information in any form and includes notes, images, audiovisual recordings, x-rays, books, documents maps, drawings, photographs, letters, vouchers and papers and any other information that is written, photographed, recorded or stored in any manner, but does not include software or any mechanism that produces records;[26]

Although there are some differences, the definitions of the above terms in the Manitoba and Saskatchewan health information legislation are fairly similar to the Alberta definitions.

However, the Alberta definition of health information differs from Manitoba and Saskatchewan in that "health services provider information" is included in Alberta. The Alberta definition of "health services provider information" is extensive and includes information such as name, address, telephone number, date of birth, unique identification number, licence number, education, continued competencies, decisions of professional bodies and business arrangements relating to payments of accounts.[27] The Ontario draft also applies to information about health providers.

Notwithstanding the definitions provided in some provinces for health information legislation, the more specific requirements are still located in health sector legislation. An example of health sector legislation that says what is included in health information exists in the regulations under the *Public Hospitals Act* in New Brunswick.[28]

The New Brunswick regulations says the board of every hospital is required to have compiled for each patient a medical record, including identification, history of present illness, history of previous illness, family history, provisional diagnosis, orders for treatment, progress notes, reports of condition on discharge, consultations, laboratory examinations, medical, surgical obstetrical and radiological treatment, operations and anaesthesia, physical examinations, radiological examinations and

---

[24] *Ibid.*, s. 1(1)(u).

[25] Alta. Reg. 70/2001.

[26] *Supra*, n. 21, s. 1(1)(t).

[27] *Ibid.*, s. 1(1)(o).

[28] N.B. Reg. 92-84.

post mortem examination, if any, final diagnosis, and such other items as the Minister may prescribe.[29] Similar provisions exist in most provinces.[30]

Provincial legislative requirements must be followed regardless of whether the information is needed or not for clinical or other purposes. However, the requirements are to be regarded as a minimum standard only. The records consist not only of information required by legislation, but also information required for other purposes such as audit, teaching, research and accreditation.

In addition to the information kept as part of the patient's record, provincial legislation may also require other information to be recorded either as part of the patient's record or recorded separately. The legislation is directed either at health providers or at government agencies. Much of this information is required for reporting to government agencies.

An example of this type of requirement arises in vital statistics legislation and requires detailed information to be reported about births, stillbirths, adoptions, marriages, changes of name and changes of sex and deaths.[31] Public health legislation requires reporting of communicable notifiable diseases. Government health insurance plans require certain records to be kept upon which payments are based.[32]

HOSPITAL AND OTHER BY-LAWS

Legislation is enacted not only by federal and provincial parliaments and legislatures, but by institutions created by those legislatures. Therefore, corporations, whether they be public or private, are given the authority to enact by-laws for the governing of their internal affairs. The by-laws must be adopted according to the procedure established in the articles of the incorporating documents of the corporation. They must not contravene any provincial or federal act or regulation. The by-laws must also not deal with any subject outside the purpose for which the corporation has been established. If these criteria are met, by-laws are valid internal legislation and may be enforced by the courts.

In the health sector, by-laws passed by hospital boards have a greater effect on the daily operations of a facility than any provincial or federal legislation. This is due, no doubt, to the fact that by-laws are often more

---

[29] *Ibid.*, s. 20.

[30] See *e.g.*, R.R.O. 1990, Reg. 965, s. 19; Sask. Reg. 331/79, s. 12(3); N.S. Reg. 16/79, ss. 15-16; N.B. Reg. 72-84, s. 20; R.R.N.W.T. Reg. 1990, c. T-12, s. 73; B.C. Reg. 121/97, s. 13; Alta. Reg. 247/90, s. 13; Man. Reg. 337/88, s. 60; O.C. 1320-84, ss. 53-57, 4 July 1984, G.O.Q. 1984.II.2347; P.E.I. Reg. EC 574/76, s. 37; Y.T.O.I.C. 1994/227, ss. 12-13.

[31] See *e.g.*, *Vital Statistics Act*, R.S.A. 2000, c. V-4, ss. 2-22.

[32] See *e.g.*, B.C. Reg. 25/61, ss. 5.2-5.9. All provinces have similar provisions.

specific. By-laws may outline information which is to be included in the health record. If the province has legislation on this matter, the by-laws may duplicate and extend legislation. The by-law requirements cannot nullify provincial legislation.

The wording of by-laws is often in the same format as legislation. The Manitoba model by-laws read as follows:[33]

> The record shall include any of the following which are pertinent or necessary to justify the diagnosis and treatment of the case involved:
>
> 1. identification data,
> 2. entrance complaint and history of present illness,
> 3. personal and family history,
> 4. physical examination report,
> 5. all special reports including:
>   (i) consultations,
>   (ii) clinical laboratory and pathology reports,
>   (iii) x-ray interpretations,
> 6. provincial diagnosis,
> 7. operative, anaesthetic, and obstetrical reports,
> 8. orders for treatment,
> 9. progress notes,
> 10. final diagnosis and discharge summary, and
> 11. autopsy report, where applicable.[34]

The Manitoba guidelines go further by requiring a complete physical examination and case history report from the attending physician within twenty-four hours after admission.[35] In addition, the model by-laws define what information is to be included in operative reports,[36] obstetrical records[37] and progress notes.[38] Operative reports shall include a pre-operative diagnosis, proposed procedure, procedure performed, findings at operation and a post-operative diagnosis.

ACCREDITATION

The requirements set forth for record keeping by the Canadian Council on Health Services Accreditation (CCHSA) also help to define what constitutes health information. The current accreditation guidelines focus on

---

[33] *Guidelines for the Development of By-laws for Health Agencies in Manitoba* (Manitoba Health Services Commission, 1978).

[34] *Ibid.*, s. 5.1(b).

[35] *Ibid.*, s. 52.

[36] *Ibid.*, s. 54.

[37] *Ibid.*, s. 55.

[38] *Ibid.*, s. 56.

objectives and goals. However, earlier versions of these guidelines gave a detailed description of what was to be included in the record as health information.

For example, in *Long Term Care I Facilities*,[39] what was then called the Canadian Council on Health Facilities Accreditation (CCHFA) indicated that the health record should include the following preadmission data:

- preadmission assessments
- transfer information if admission is from a hospital or other health care facility
- admission history and physical examination
- physician's initial orders for medication, treatment and diet
- personal information, including the name of the next of kin or responsible party
- consent forms (if required)
- admission agreement
- lifestyle and social history

The same accreditation guide required specific documentation to meet the needs of residents.[40] This included:

- interdisciplinary team assessments
- multidisciplinary progress notes
- current, signed medication and treatment orders
- physician progress notes written on each visit
- results of diagnostic tests and examinations
- annual physical examinations
- medication records
- reports from consultants
- readmission and transfer information following a temporary admission to hospital

Other guides published by CCHFA also addressed the issue of health care record keeping. For example, in *Acute Care Hospitals, 1991*,[41] documentation was quite specific for intensive care, chronic care unit and transplant units. Patient care records had to include, among other items, an initial assessment, a care plan, progress notes, flow charts and evidence of support for the patient's family.[42]

---

[39] *Long Term Care I Facilities*, Ottawa: CCHFA, 1990, at 20.
[40] *Ibid.*
[41] *Acute Care Hospitals, 1991*, Ottawa: CCHFA, 1990, at 274.
[42] *Ibid.*

OTHER REQUIREMENTS

In determining the appropriate health information content for the record, a review should be made of all federal and provincial acts and regulations appropriate to the particular health provider, hospital by-laws where appropriate and the accreditation guidelines. Contracts to provide home care services, arrangements with firms performing service utilization profiles, and insurance agreements should be incorporated in the record. The same can be said of customary practice in a health agency or guidelines set by professional organizations. These standards establish the basic minimum content.

Much depends, however, on the "setting" in which the health information is used and generated. For example, the content of a student's health record in a school setting will be quite different from that found in a hospital setting. By the same token even within the same health agency the requirements for documenting discharge planning may vary from one unit to another. Detailed information may be provided to a day surgery or emergency room patient who leaves hospital with a follow-up instruction sheet including warning signs, post-discharge care recommendations, and telephone numbers to call if complications arise. The same may not be true of a person leaving hospital after a non-invasive course of therapy.

For purposes of continuity of care and legal defence, the fact that discharge planning occurred and that follow-up instructions were provided should be noted. Indeed, in many cases it may be appropriate to either include the follow-up instruction sheet or note the form number in the notes. In this way evidence of communicating important discharge information to patients is entrenched.

The next step is to take into consideration the purposes for which the information is needed. Each purpose may require further information beyond that already required. This can be determined by seeking the advice of those who are directly involved in carrying out that purpose, whether it is care, teaching, research or auditing. It is particularly important to seek the advice of all disciplines involved. The nursing staff, or the dietary staff may require the inclusion of very different information from that required by the medical staff, even though all are involved in care and treatment.

The purpose of legal defence will require information that may not be required for any other purpose. Most documents that may be used for the defence of a lawsuit are primarily used for other purposes, usually for care and treatment. However, there are some exceptions. (See Chapter 6 — Health Information as Evidence.)

The first example is the consent to treatment form[43] which serves as evidence, though not always conclusive, that the patient has consented to the treatment. The second example is the waiver of liability. This document signed by the patient may exonerate the hospital and its staff from responsibility when the patient refuses to accept recommended treatment or leaves the facility against medical advice. The last example is acknowledgment by the patient that certain possessions are in the hands of the facility. This information assists to defend the facility against a suit alleging the loss of items not on the list and may limit the liability of the facility.

This information may not always be in the form of documents signed by the patient. The patient may be incapable of signing or unwilling to sign. Instead a record of the event which would ordinarily lead to such documents is made by staff. This step is done mainly for communication with family and for legal defence, and forms part of the overall record.

ORGANIZATION OF THE INFORMATION

Lawyers are often asked whether certain information should be included in the patient's chart or should be kept separately. Some records have a temporary purpose while other records have a longer use. In most cases there is no legal answer, since this is mostly an administrative issue rather than a legal question. Obviously, if legislative requirements exist such as under the *Narcotic Control Regulations* to maintain information in a particular way, such directives must be followed.

The issue is particularly contentious when it involves matters such as self-charting by patients or incident reports. Some believe that entries made by patients may be inaccurate, inflammatory, and lead to litigation. Others believe that such entries provide valuable insights into patient care. The answer sometimes exists in provincial legislation, health facility by-laws, and practice standards.

Incident reports and other risk management documents are another matter. As seen in Chapter 17 — Risk Management in Health Information, incident reports were intended as administrative documents to identify deficiencies in care. The idea was to use this data to improve care. Over time, such reports have become contentious documents. As a plaintiff's lawyer could use such documents to augment a negligence claim, this makes a strong case for keeping incident reports out of the health record. Unless provincial law requires otherwise, it may be best to

---

[43] L.E. and F.A. Rozovsky, *The Canadian Law of Consent to Treatment* (Toronto: Butterworths Canada, 1990).

keep this type of administrative document separate from the health record.

PRACTICAL CONSIDERATIONS

When determining the information that is to be documented as part of the health record, the following considerations should be kept in mind:

1. *Legislative Requirements* — Requirements in relevant provisions in statutes, regulations and by-laws must be reviewed and incorporated as a part of the health information in the record.
2. *Other Standards* — Standards that arise from sources such as accreditation, contractual agreements, professional standards and standards of practice from the specific area involved should be considered when determining the health information that should be included in the record.
3. *Administrative Considerations* — Decisions regarding the health information that is to be included in the record should be based upon considerations that include the purposes such as care, education, research and legal defence, and practical considerations such as the ability to expeditiously locate health information when needed.

4

Standards for Health Information

Standards of health information refer not only to what is recorded, but what is not. How information is collected and recorded, who collects and records it, when it is collected and recorded, how the record is kept and how the information is transmitted and communicated all relate to standards. (See Chapter 3 — What Is Health information?) Standards for maintaining health information are found in a number of sources.

PROFESSIONAL PRACTICE STANDARDS

The first and perhaps the most important standard is that of current professional practice standards in the province or territory and throughout Canada. Experts in health records administration and in the area of practice involved should be consulted for current developments in the field. Some standards for tertiary care teaching hospitals may be the same as for rural community hospitals. In other instances standards may be very different. However, one cannot assume that standards for different types of providers are automatically different. In any case, these standards are constantly changing and, therefore, must be regularly reviewed.

The Canadian Health Record Association (CHRA) is an excellent resource for professional standards of practice. The CHRA has published position statements and recommendations for access and release of health information,[1] safeguarding health information,[2] record security,[3] computerization,[4] electronic transmission of health information,[5] record completion[6] and data quality.[7] The Canadian College of Health Record

---

[1] *Patient Access to Health Records* (Don Mills: CHRA, 1985); *Principles and Guidelines for Access to and Release of Health Information* (Don Mills: CHRA, 1995).

[2] *Code of Practice for Safeguarding Health Information* (Don Mills: CHRA, 1980).

[3] *Record Security* (Don Mills: CHRA, 1987).

[4] *Security of Computerized Health Information* (Don Mills: CHRA, 1989).

[5] *Electronic Transmission of Health Information* (Don Mills: CHRA, 1999).

[6] *Record Completion* (Don Mills: CHRA, 1990).

[7] *Data Quality* (Don Mills: CHRA, 1993).

Administrators has also established a *Code of Ethics* for its members.[8] Provincial health record associations may also be of assistance.

Clinical groups have also developed guidelines that address standards of practice. This includes the Ontario College of Physicians and Surgeons in their volume on practice standards for health care agencies operating under the *Independent Health Facilities Act*.[9] Various professional associations and colleges have published standards that relate to professional duties relating to medical records.[10]

With many medical specialty groups developing and implementing clinical practice guidelines or standards, it is reasonable to expect that these standards will include provisions dealing with health care information. Anaesthesiology, pediatrics, and obstetrics are likely areas for standards development.

It is not a sufficient legal excuse however, to claim that the common practice was followed, if the common practice itself is negligent.[11]

With so many groups engaged in setting and implementing practice standards, there is a good chance that provisions governing health care information could clash with health facility documentation requirements. This risk can be reasonably anticipated, and should be addressed proactively to avoid confusion and controversy.

ACCREDITATION STANDARDS

A second source of standards is the accreditation program of the Canadian Council on Health Services Accreditation (CCHSA) (formerly the Canadian Council on Health Facilities Accreditation (CCHFA))[12] and other accreditation programs. Care should be taken not to confuse the standards of the Canadian Council with its American counterpart, the Joint Commission on Accreditation of Healthcare Organizations

CCHSA ≈ JCAHO

---

[8] *Code of Ethics* (Don Mills: CHRA, 1985, revd. 1989).

[9] R.S.O. 1990, c. I.3. See *IHDF Clinical Practice Parameters & Facility Standards* (Toronto: Ontario College of Physicians and Surgeons, 1991).

[10] See *e.g.*, Canadian Medical Association, *The Medical Record: Confidentiality, Access and Disclosure* (May 9, 2000); Alberta Medical Association, *Clinical Practice Guidelines*; College of Physicians and Surgeons of Alberta, *Physicians' Office Medical Records: CPSA Policy* (revised February 2000); College of Physicians and Surgeons of Alberta, *Release of Medical Information: A Guide for Alberta Physicians* (revised March 2002); College of Physicians and Surgeons of Alberta, *Reporting Unfit Drivers* (revised June 1996); College of Physicians and Surgeons of Alberta, *The Referral/Consultation Process* (issued March 1996).

[11] *ter Neuzen v. Korn*, [1995] 3 S.C.R. 674, 127 D.L.R. (4th) 577.

[12] Note that the Council operates a number of different accreditation programmes for services as diverse as acute care, long term care, home care, medical facilities in prisons, etc.

(JCAHO). The approach of the two organizations can be quite different. The American approach tends to be more specific in what an accredited facility must or must not do. The Canadian approach focuses on the object and goals, which should be achieved. The accreditation process is designed to determine whether those objects and goals are being achieved. The result is that two facilities or services may take very different approaches and yet both meet accreditation standards.

Failure to meet accreditation standards in a service or facility that has been surveyed and accredited by the Council may itself be considered as negligence in failing to meet appropriate standards.

AGENCY STANDARDS

A third source of standards is found in specialized standard setting agencies and entities that influence specialized activities, such as human research. For example in regards to research, reference should be made to statements and publications of the Tri-Council. The Tri-Council is composed of the Medical Research Council of Canada (MRC), Natural Sciences and Engineering Research Council of Canada (NSERC) and the Social Sciences and Humanities Research Council of Canada (SSHRC).[13] Publications of the Canadian Institutes of Health Research (CIHR)[14] should also be referenced.

LEGISLATIVE AND REGULATORY STANDARDS

A fourth source of standards is legislation and regulations. (See Chapter 3 — What Is Health Information?) Jurisdictions with health information privacy legislation are governed by a provincial legislative standard that applies to many types of health records, health services and groups of health professionals.[15] These legislative regimes create detailed rules for

---

[13] *Tri-Council Policy Statement: Ethical Conduct for Research Involving Humans* (Ottawa: Medical Research Council of Canada, 1998) at 1-9. Note that CIHR has recently replaced MRC as a member of the Council.

[14] P. Kosseim, ed. *A Compendium of Canadian Legislation Respecting the Protection of Personal Information in Health Research* (Ottawa: Canadian Institutes of Health Research, 2000; *Personal Information Protection and Electronic Documents Act: Questions and Answers for Health Researchers* (Ottawa: Canadian Institutes of Health Research, 2001); *Selected International Legal Norms on the Protection of Personal Information in Health Research* (Ottawa: Canadian Institutes of Health Research, December 2001).

[15] *The Personal Health Information Act*, S.M. 1997, c. 51 (C.C.S.M., c. P33.5), *Health Information Act*, R.S.A. 2000, c. H-5, *Health Information Protection Act*, S.S. 1999, c. H-0.021 (enacted but not proclaimed); *Draft Privacy of Personal Information Act, 2000*, Ontario.

the access, collection, use, disclosure and safeguarding of health records. For example, all of these regimes require the custodian or trustee to make a reasonable effort to ensure that the health record is complete and accurate.[16]

As discussed in Chapter 3, legislation and regulations may relate to the particular service and may require particular information to be placed in the record. Such requirements are not always restricted to the quantitative content.

In this way legislation attempts to influence the quality of care by requiring that information on a number of items be recorded. However, one cannot rely solely on compliance with legislation or regulations. Quality care will not be maintained, let alone improved, merely by documenting various items of health information as required by law.

The information must be referred to by the appropriate individuals, at the appropriate time, interpreted in the appropriate manner and used in the appropriate way. The legislative or regulatory requirements only require that the information be documented to enable these other steps to happen.

Legislation and regulations set only the minimum standard. Additional information required by other standards, such as professional practice and accreditation, must also be included.

Legislation has been used to establish standards for when records must be made and who must prepare records. An example exists in the 1980 Saskatchewan *Hospital Standards Regulations*, which state:[17]

> 13(1) The attending physician shall complete the discharge summary of the patient's health record within seven days after the patient's separation.
>
> (2) The patient's health record shall be completed and signed by the attending physician or the physician designated by the attending physician within twenty-one days of the patient's separation.
>
> (3) Each physician shall sign those parts of the health record for which he is responsible.
>
> (4) The attending physician shall read and if necessary alter entries made by medical intern or JURSI (Junior Undergraduate Rotating Student Intern) staff and shall then sign the patient's health record to indicate that it has been properly completed.[18]

Saskatchewan also regulates the method by which certain types of records must be prepared, for example:

---

[16] *Ibid.*

[17] Sask. Reg. 331/79.

[18] *Ibid.*, s. 13.

17. Each order made by a physician, including standing orders, or individual sets of orders shall be recorded in ink and signed by the physician so ordering and shall become part of the patient's health record.[19]

In addition to the usual list of required contents Saskatchewan directs that various services must be recorded:

23. Physical therapy services provided on the order of a physician shall be recorded and the record shall become part of the patient's health record.[20]

In an attempt to encourage the accuracy of patient records, British Columbia has enacted the following clause as part of its *Hospital Act*[21] relating to private hospitals.

18 (3) A person must not do any of the following:
   (a) knowingly make an untrue entry in the register of patients;
   (b) destroy, damage or mutilate a register of patients or any part of it;
   (c) delete or alter a true and correct entry appearing in a register of patients, or fail to make an entry required to be made under this Part.[22]

In provinces in which statutory or regulatory provisions do not exist, similar directives may be included in hospital by-laws, rules or policies or procedures of a particular health facility. Even in those provinces with statutory or regulatory provisions there may be in-house rules duplicating the statute or regulation. This is not always wise since it creates the possibility of the statute or regulation changing without a similar change being made in-house. The statute or regulation takes precedence, but the staff may not be aware of the enactment. The wording may also be slightly different, creating the impression that the meaning may be different.

Where no written directives of any type exist, professional standards and accepted practice alone may be followed.

NEGLIGENCE LAW

The word "negligence" is often used by lawyers and laymen without a clear understanding of its meaning. Learned treatises have refined the

---

[19] *Ibid.*, s. 17.
[20] *Ibid.*, s. 20.
[21] R.S.B.C. 1996, c. 200.
[22] *Ibid.*, s. 18(3).

meaning of the word to such an extent that for the purposes of ordinary life, practical implications are lost. This may also be true for the Quebec civil law counterpart under the *Civil Code*.[23]

As a basic premise the wrongful act of negligence must fulfill five criteria. These criteria are outlined by Professor John G. Fleming in *The Law of Torts*.[24]

1.   There must be a duty recognized by law to conduct one's self in accordance with a certain standard.
2.   There must be a breach of that duty, that is that the person has failed to live up to that standard.
3.   The person to whom the duty is owed must be injured.
4.   There must be a reasonably proximate connection between the failure to live up to the proper standards and the injury.
5.   The injured party must not have done anything which would make his injuries worse.[25]

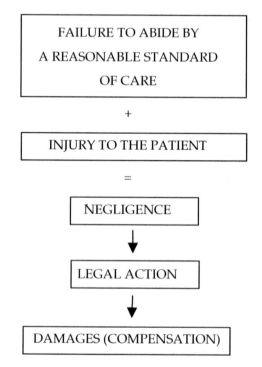

FAILURE TO ABIDE BY

A REASONABLE STANDARD

OF CARE

+

INJURY TO THE PATIENT

=

NEGLIGENCE

↓

LEGAL ACTION

↓

DAMAGES (COMPENSATION)

---

[23]   Art. 1457 C.C.Q.
[24]   9th ed. (Sydney: LBC Information Services, 1998), at 115-116.
[25]   *Ibid.*

The basic standard of care required is that of the "reasonable person of ordinary prudence."[26] Applying this standard to any person or institution supplying a specialized service, the duty is higher than for a service that is not specialized. According to Fleming, "those who undertake work calling for special skill must not only exercise reasonable care but measure up to the standard of proficiency that can be expected from such professionals."[27]

It is generally recognized that record keeping is an integral part of the care, diagnosis and treatment of a patient. Without records staff are not always able to communicate with one another regarding the patient's condition and what should or should not be done for the patient. Without records staff would also not be able to remember information which would affect their own actions.

Many interventions are based on the information in the health records. The well-being of the patient depends on this information and the patient can be placed at risk of injury without correct information.

Five errors can be made with respect to the compilation and utilization of the patient record:

(1) information which is required for the care and treatment of the patient is omitted;
(2) incorrect information is placed in the record;
(3) information which is required by a particular staff member or service for the patient's care or treatment is not transferred to them;
(4) personnel fail to read recorded information; and
(5) personnel read the record incorrectly either through carelessness on the part of the reader or illegibility on the part of the recorder.

Each of these errors can cause patient injury. For example, the failure to note or to read the note that a patient is allergic to a particular drug may result in injury and even death of the patient. Similar injuries can take place through errors in the record relating to the dosage of a drug.

Applying negligence principles, it is clear that since it is reasonably foreseeable that such injuries may occur when such errors are made, there is a duty on the health provider not to make these errors, or at least to take reasonable steps to minimize that possibility. Failure to take these steps may be shown to be a breach of the duty by not providing this aspect of care and treatment in an average, reasonable and prudent manner. If injury

---

[26] *Ibid.*, at 117.
[27] *Ibid.*, at 121.

has resulted, it may be found that the provider was negligent and therefore liable to compensate the patient for the resulting injuries.[28]

An example of negligence in record keeping resulting in liability is
seen in *Meyer v. Gordon*,[29] a 1981 British Columbia Supreme Court case.
Mr. Justice Legg stated:

> The lack of care, the inadequate charting, and the unsatisfactory evi-
> dence to which I have referred establish liability for negligence on the
> defendant Hospital.[30]

The 1982 British Columbia Supreme Court decision of *Wipfli v. Brit-
ten*[31] criticized the doctor's record keeping:

> However, I find that Dr. Britten's practice of recording Mrs. Wipfli's
> fundal height by means of a diagram, his failure to record the fundal
> height and other usual obstetrical information on the running chart
> for the November 7 visit, and the practice of.... making the notations
> on the prenatal chart, all contributed in some degree to Dr. Britten's
> failing to diagnose that Mrs. Wipfli was carrying twins.[32]
>
>   . . .
>
> Under the circumstances of this case I am satisfied that his failure to
> diagnose twins was not in accord with the reasonable standard of care
> of a family physician practising in Vancouver in 1975-76. I conclude
> that he was negligent.[33]

It must, therefore, be concluded that in any preventive liability, risk or
quality management program, special attention must be paid to the quality
of record keeping. This applies not only to records maintained in a health
institution but equally to records maintained in private offices of physicians
and dentists, community clinics, correctional facilities and school health
services.

---

[28] For further discussion see *Salmond & Heuston on the Law of Torts*, 21st ed. (London:
Sweet & Maxwell, 1996), c. 9 and A.M. Linden, *Canadian Tort Law*, 7th ed. (Toronto:
Butterworths, 2001) cc. 4 and 5.

[29] (1981), 17 C.C.L.T. 1 (B.C.S.C.).

[30] *Ibid.*, at 53.

[31] (1982), 22 C.C.L.T. 104 (B.C.S.C.).

[32] *Ibid.*, *per* Hinds J., at 115.

[33] *Ibid.*, at 123.

5

Retention, Storage and Disposal

ISSUES

Questions that are frequently raised by health record administrators and physicians in private practice are: how long should health information be retained and stored? Can the information be microfilmed and if so, can the hard copy be destroyed? How long should the microfilms be kept? Can part of the information be destroyed? Is there a particular method that must be used to destroy the health information?

There is no simple answer. However, the answer for each setting can be determined and a policy formulated by examining the purposes for which the health information is kept. When developing policies on retention, storage and disposal, the question must be asked: why is the information needed? Health information must be retained and stored for as long as it is required to fulfill key purposes.

The first portion of this chapter deals with the retention of health information. The second addresses the storage of health information such as microfilming. The third addresses the disposal of health information.

RETENTION

All health information is required for more than one purpose. It is suggested that a maximum retention period should be established for each main purpose for which health information is maintained. The longest retention period will cover other retention periods. It must be remembered that each type of health information is not collected, used or disclosed for the same purposes.

It is possible that parts of the information should be retained for one period, while other parts of the information should be kept for other periods of time. If doubt exists as to the length of the retention period, the longer time should be applied. (See Chapter 2 — Purposes of Health Information, for a discussion of the purposes for which health information is kept.)

Legislative retention periods must be met. In private offices generating taxable income, Revenue Canada and provincial taxation authorities may review income tax returns for a number of years after they have been submitted. Supporting documents may be needed to defend the return. Advice from the taxation authorities should be sought in writing as the retention requirements may change from year to year.

At present, documents should be kept for a minimum of eight years for purposes of federal income tax as a complaint can be laid for up to eight years after a matter arises — not the date on which the income was either earned or received.[1] It is possible for taxation officials to pursue claims beyond that period. Before any decision is made as to the destruction of taxation records, either written authorization should be received from taxation officials or expert advice should be obtained such as from an accountant familiar with your area of business.

Enactments and guidelines across the country, both at the provincial and federal level, require health service providers to prepare and retain various types of health information. However, often it is not clear how long information should or must be kept. Legislation that creates a minimum retention period often does not prevent retention for a longer period. If other purposes for which the information is kept require a longer retention period, the longer period should be established.

Different retention periods may exist for different types of health information such as information relating to assisted reproduction, medical devices or blood products. For example, the Health Canada Directive on the Technical Requirements for Therapeutic Donor Insemination requires that medical records regarding the donor be kept indefinitely.[2] Retention periods for employee health information may be radically different depending upon the employer and whether industrial health risks exist to which occupational health legislation applies. (For more information refer to Chapter 15 — Employee Health Information).

Some provinces have extremely detailed regulations dealing with retention of health information in hospitals while other provinces leave the matter to hospital policy. Detailed legislative requirements exist in the regulations[3] under the Ontario *Public Hospitals Act*,[4] that specifies different retention periods for different categories of information such as for inpatients, outpatients and persons under 18 years of age. In contrast, less detailed retention requirements exist in Saskatchewan under the *Hospital Standards Regulation*.[5]

Prince Edward Island has extremely detailed legislative requirements for retention of hospital health information. The *Hospital Management*

---

[1] *Income Tax Act*, R.S.C. 1985, c. 1 (5th Supp.), s. 244(4).
[2] Technical Requirements for Therapeutic Donor Insemination, Health Canada Directive, July 2000.
[3] R.R.O. 1990, Reg. 965, s. 20.
[4] R.S.O. 1990, c. P.40.
[5] R.R.S. 1979, Reg. 331, s. 15.

Regulations[6] require hard copies of medical records that have been photographed to be kept for two years after discharge or death.[7] Photographs must be kept 50 years from the date they were made.[8] A statutory declaration must be made under oath when health records are destroyed.[9]

In Prince Edward Island hospitals, original records that have not been photographed must be kept for 20 years after discharge or five years after death.[10] The retention period for a person under 18 years does not begin to run until the individual reaches 18 years of age.[11] Some types of health information do not need to be retained such as nurses notes and TPR sheets unless a court action has begun or a misadventure has occurred.[12] X-ray films must be kept five years if there is a significant abnormality or a court action, but otherwise for one year.[13]

Where retention periods are not prescribed by legislation, retention rules must be established by examining all the purposes of maintaining health information. Retention periods need to be established in all types of health settings such as in pharmacies, physiotherapy clinics, public health, long term care, lodges and assisted living. Some provinces such as Alberta and Saskatchewan are working toward the development of province-wide regulations to establish retention periods for health information. The trend is toward longer retention periods for health care purposes due to latent disease manifestations, for example in tuberculosis, syphilis, polio, medical devices and blood products and for genetic reasons.

One questions whether legislative retention periods achieve anything other than providing minimum guidelines. Guidelines could be established through government advice or accreditation bodies. The disadvantage of legislation is that it applies to all situations within the scope of the legislation whether or not it is appropriate. Minimum legislative standards may be too low in some cases and too high in others. Complex legislation with different retention periods can create administrative problems, such as the time required to review and categorize the type of health information.

Limitation periods must be considered when establishing retention periods. Since health information is essential when defending legal proceedings, this information must be retained as long as there is a possibility of legal action being brought by a patient, family or guardian. The

---

[6] R.R.P.E.I. EC 574/76.
[7] *Ibid.*, s. 41(2) and (3).
[8] *Ibid.*
[9] *Ibid.*, s. 42.
[10] *Ibid.*, s. 43.
[11] *Ibid.*, s. 44.
[12] *Ibid.*, s. 45.
[13] *Ibid.*, s. 46.

possibility of litigation exists until the limitation period has run its course. This is the period during which an individual who feels wronged by another can take legal action. Once the period has run, the action is statute barred and cannot be commenced.

The purpose of a limitation period is to bring peace to the parties. The injustice which the wrongdoer might have caused is eventually outweighed by the injustice of having a potential lawsuit threatening indefinitely. It is designed to force the injured party to take action or forget about it.

Every province has statutory limitation periods. Limitation periods differ depending on the type of legal action that is being brought and the defendant. The periods vary from province to province so that an action brought against a particular class of defendant, such as a physician or hospital, is different depending on the province or territory. In most provinces the limitation period is outlined in the Limitation of Actions Act. In Quebec, the limitation period is set out in the *Civil Code*.

Limitation periods may also be set out in acts dealing with the specific class to which the defendant belongs. Limitation periods specified in hospital, medical and other special acts overrule the more general provisions of a Limitation of Actions Act.[14] For example, in Saskatchewan the *Hospital Standards Act*[15] creates a three-month limitation period for hospitals unless a court application is made within one year from the date the damages were sustained.[16]

Limitations of Actions Acts ordinarily have provisions that delay the limitation period. An example of this type of provision may be found in British Columbia's *Limitation Act*.[17] The Act deals with the potential plaintiff who is either a minor or a person incapable of or substantially impeded in the management of his or her affairs. In such a case the limitation period fixed by that act is postponed as long as the person remains under such a disability to a limit of six years. Such a postponement would not apply to limitation periods set out in statutes other than the Limitation Act.

It is important to determine the act under which the limitation period falls for the particular health care provider or facility in question. One must not assume that the time period for all personnel or all facilities will necessarily be the same. In other words, the limitation period for an action brought by a patient under the age of majority against a physician may not be the same as for an action brought by the same patient against

---

[14] J.S. Williams, *Limitation of Actions in Canada*, 2nd ed. (Toronto: Butterworths, 1980), at 43.

[15] R.S.S. 1978, c. H-10.

[16] *Ibid.*, s. 15.

[17] R.S.B.C. 1979, c. 236, s. 7.

a nurse or a hospital. The limitation period may be different depending on the legal action in question, such as contract or negligence.

In determining the time period during which information may be needed for legal defence purposes, the first question that must be answered is: who are the potential defendants? In a facility setting, the facility itself is an obvious target for alleged wrongdoing. Employees may be sued in their individual capacities, such as self-employed physicians who work in the facility but for whom the facility is not ordinarily responsible. The period during which each category of defendant can be sued and the possibilities for extension of those periods, must be determined. A retention period can then be chosen to cover all likely circumstances.

Special care must be taken in determining the point at which the time period begins to run. From an administrative point of view, this is particularly important to enable staff to know with certainty when the period is over and when retention is no longer necessary. Traditionally limitation periods commenced when the course of action arose. Special limitation periods prescribed for health facilities and providers usually begin to run from the time the patient is discharged or stops receiving treatment.

It may be difficult to determine when the patient ceases to receive treatment especially if treatment has been given over a long period of time on an outpatient basis. This problem is a factual one that is determined by the courts when asked to rule on the validity of a limitations defence. Because of the uncertainty, retention periods should not be established without consulting legal counsel.

There is concern that a patient may be injured due to negligence and the injury might not be "discovered" until the limitation period has expired. The injury may not be apparent until after the passage of the limitation period, for example in birth injuries such as cerebral palsy. Despite the fact that the injury may have been caused by negligence, no compensation would be possible since legal action would be barred.

As a result of this injustice to plaintiffs, limitation periods in Canada have generally adopted the "discovery rule". This rule states that the limitation period does not begin to run until the wrongful act is discovered or could reasonably have been discovered. The *Civil Code* in Quebec for example, says:

> 2260a In matters of medical or hospital responsibility, the action in indemnity for bodily or mental prejudice caused to a patient is prescribed by three years from the date of the fault. However, if the prejudice becomes apparent gradually, the delay runs only from the day on which it first appeared.[18]

---

[18] Art. 2260a C.C.Q.

Discovery rules have been adopted in many provinces and territories, for example in British Columbia,[19] Manitoba,[20] Nova Scotia[21] and Alberta.[22] The limitation rules do not apply to all potential defendants providing health care. British Columbia places a limit of six years on the extension insofar as hospitals are concerned,[23] Nova Scotia has a four-year limit on all extensions,[24] and Alberta has a 10-year limit.[25]

Open-ended discovery rules, which allow actions to be brought for an unlimited period of time, cause great difficulty in determining how long health information should be retained for defence purposes. An arbitrary period must be chosen following consultation with legal counsel and insurers. Discovery rules, which allow for a maximum extension, make the record retention decision easier. In those jurisdictions the retention period should be at least for that maximum length of time.

There is concern that the lengthened limitation periods could contribute to a medical malpractice crisis in Canada. Despite the fact that litigation is increasing, insurance premiums and the availability of malpractice insurance do not appear to have been a problem. Most physicians in Canada do not carry malpractice insurance but rather are members of the Canadian Medical Protective Association. Some provinces have set up their own provincial liability plans.

STORAGE

Photographing health information onto microfilm has been carried out by hundreds of health facilities across Canada for many years. The main purpose of microfilming is to save space, which can be as much as 98 per cent. Microfilming provides a method of storing information, which is easier to retrieve than searching through bulky files of documents.

Microfilming provides a form of security that is not available with hard copy or paper health records, from which individual documents or pages could be removed or altered. This is particularly important when considering unauthorized third party access.

There are a number of microfilm methods. Each method has advantages and disadvantages of cost, time, ease and speed of access and retrieval, and amount of labour required. Regardless of the system, the

---

[19] *Limitations Act*, R.S.B.C. 1979, c. 236, ss. 6, 8.
[20] *Limitation of Actions Act*, R.S.M. 1987, c. L150, ss. 14-20.
[21] *Limitation of Actions Act*, R.S.N.S. 1989, c. 258, s. 3.
[22] *Limitations Act*, R.S.A. 2000, c. L-12.
[23] *Supra*, n. 19, s. 8.
[24] *Supra*, n. 21.
[25] *Supra*, n. 22, s. 3(1)(b).

quality of the microfilm is always dependent on the condition of the original document and on the controls used during filming and processing. Quality is better preserved on microfilm than in the original paper record which will deteriorate, especially with handling.

There are evidentiary rules that must be considered when making decisions about microfilming health information. (See Chapter 6 — Health Information as Evidence.) For example, the various jurisdictions have requirements regarding authenticity and admissibility that relate to whether the original records must still be kept after microfilming. Only after such a retention period is over should the originals be destroyed. The typical six-year retention requirement for originals does not apply to governments or health facilities that are part of a provincial or federal department.[26]

There are various modes of storage depending upon how health information is already stored such as on magnetic tapes, photographs or fluoroscopy. The choice of method of storage must take into account the longevity of the medium as well as requirements such as readers for the medium that may not be available for as long as the retention period. The retention period for any method of storage should be established in the same way as the retention period for original health information since the film or other medium is a substitute for the original. After the retention period is over the film or other storage medium may be destroyed.

RETENTION AND STORAGE OF COMPUTER INFORMATION

Many health agencies are moving in the direction of electronic health information. This is the case for hospitals and nursing homes with bedside terminals as well as for physicians and home care nurses with laptop computers and palm pilots for direct data entry.

The elimination of hard copy information is seen as having the potential for saving considerable time and money. The software available in the health care field is impressive and enables health providers to send information from patient to computer such as fetal monitoring strips and to call up analysis or comparative data. While the computer is not intended to eliminate the duty of the caregiver to carefully assess each patient, it does have the potential to facilitate quality patient care.

Computer-based health information is discussed at greater length later on. (See Chapter 9 — Computerization and Information Linkage.)

---

[26] *Evidence Act*, R.S.B.C. 1979, c. 116; *Alberta Evidence Act*, R.S.A. 2000, c. A-18.

Central to the discussion here is the issue of retention of health information, which is made easier by automatic transmission to hard drives or back-up discs. How long should the computer information be retained? In what format? What are the rules that govern the transmission of computer information to long-term storage?

The law is often in a catch-up mode, trying to keep up with changes in the mores of society and its technology. Legislators have not contemplated if computer information should be kept for a different length of time than hard copy. Little thought may have been given to whether computer information should be moved off a main frame to a tape or CD ROM.

No health care agency wants to be the "test case" that is used to decide these issues. A prudent approach is to obtain cogent answers to these questions as part of the planning process for the change from paper files to computerized data. Advice from experts such as legal counsel, health information technology and health records is essential, not only to make certain that the information will be acceptable as a legal document, but to ensure that the format used will provide safe and cost-effective storage.

DISPOSAL

Once the retention period is over, there is no need to maintain either the original or a copy of the health information. The purposes for which the original is retained are the same purposes for which a copy is kept. If the purpose for keeping the original information no longer exists, there is no purpose for keeping a copy. It is possible that a purpose that did not exist when the information was originally collected subsequently arises such in legal proceedings. A new purpose may require a change in the retention period. If there is doubt, legal advice should be obtained.

Health facilities and providers are responsible for protecting the privacy and security of health information until the information is ef-fectively destroyed. When the information is no longer needed, the information should be destroyed. However, this is an irreversible step so a formal process should be adopted to ensure that there are no miscommunications and that the information can be destroyed. A record should be kept documenting that the information has been destroyed.

Generally accepted methods of destruction include shredding or burning of paper files and complete erasure or scrambling of computer data. Expert advice must be obtained to ensure destruction of computerized health information to ensure that the data does not still exist somewhere inadvertently such as on a computer hard drive or on the memory of a photocopier or fax machine.

PRACTICAL CONSIDERATIONS

1. *Retention* — Establishing an appropriate retention period for health information may be difficult, although the trend is toward longer retention periods. Different retention periods exist for various types of health services, health providers, circumstances and types of health information. It is important to get expert advice when establishing retention periods for your health setting.

2. *Storage* — Various choices exist for storage of health information, although microfiche has remained a common mode.

3. *Disposal* — Health information must be effectively destroyed when the retention period expires. A formal process should be established to ensure that the information should actually be destroyed and to document the routine disposal of information.

6

Health Information as Evidence

THE PURPOSE OF EVIDENCE

The primary purpose of health information is clinical; that is, diagnostic, care, and treatment. However, health information is equally important as evidence in legal proceedings. In fact, the outcome of the proceedings may depend to a very large extent on health information. Health information has an equally valuable role in legal proceedings affecting residents of extended care institutions, as well as recipients of any type of health care regardless of the setting in which it is given.

The proceedings may be civil cases including divorce and personal injury matters, criminal prosecutions, labour arbitrations and disciplinary actions.

The purpose of this chapter is to present an overall view of health information and the role it plays in the judicial process. Those who wish in-depth information on specific evidentiary issues in particular proceedings should refer to the relevant federal and provincial evidence legislation, federal and provincial rules of court and texts specifically on the subject of evidence.

In most legal proceedings two decisions must be made. The first is to determine the facts of what happened. The second is to determine what law is applicable to those facts and then to apply it. It is the first determination where information often plays a major role. The court or other deciding tribunal attempts to reconstruct what occurred by means of witnesses testifying as to what they or others did, saw, heard or said. Physical property such as a weapon or clothing may also be brought into court as an exhibit in order to assist in the reconstruction. Documents, record photographs and recordings may also be presented.

The problem with witnesses is that they may forget what happened. They may be confused or mistaken, or they may be lying. Physical property may not always be useful either, since it is not always self-explanatory and must be interpreted by a witness. Therefore, the usefulness of physical exhibits often depends on the credibility of witnesses.

One of the most valuable pieces of evidence, however, is the health record since it is an historical account of what indeed did occur. Unlike the testimony of a witness it does not deteriorate over time. It is designed as an accurate reporting system of events for the purpose of care and treatment. As such, it equally serves the needs of legal proceedings in reconstructing these events.

Also of value is the record of a physician's report where the party to a legal proceeding was examined solely for the purpose of those proceedings, such as to determine the extent of injuries for which compensation is being claimed. This type of medical record is in a class by itself and is usually not thought of as a health record prepared in the usual practice of care and treatment. For information on this type of report, reference should be made to texts on evidence and to the rules of procedure of the courts of the various jurisdictions.

THE RULE AGAINST HEARSAY

Traditionally, only primary evidence has been allowed before the courts. The only evidence that has been permitted is that which a witness actually perceived through his or her own senses and not that gathered from other sources. Written or oral statements made by persons who are not before the court as witnesses are inadmissible, as evidence that the information contained in these statements is true.[1] For this reason health records were not admitted into court. They were in effect "hearsay".

The records contained statements of fact and opinion recorded by various individuals who were not before the court. Therefore, the credibility of these statements could not be tested by cross-examination. The statements written into the records may or may not have been true. Without the opportunity to test them, they were not admissible.

THE ARES V. VENNER EXCEPTION

There have always been exceptions to the hearsay rule.[2] In 1970 a major Supreme Court of Canada decision in the case of *Ares v. Venner* examined the question of whether hospital records, including nurses' notes, could be admissible as an exception to the hearsay rule.[3] The Court answered in the affirmative with the following rule:

> Hospital records, including nurses' notes, made contemporaneously by someone having a personal knowledge of the matters then being recorded and under a duty to make the entry of record should be re-

---

[1]   *Canadian Abridgement*, 2nd ed., vol. R15, at 133-34.
[2]   *Supra*, n. 1.
[3]   [1970] S.C.R. 608, 73 W.W.R. 347, 14 D.L.R. (3d) 4, 12 C.R.N.S. 349.

ceived in evidence as *prima facie* proof of the facts stated therein. This should, in no way, preclude a party wishing to challenge the accuracy of the records or entries from doing so.[4]

By analyzing the rule allowing hospital records to be admissible as evidence, a number of conclusions can be drawn.

1. The entries must be made at the same time as the facts, which are being recorded, occurred. It is obvious that this is not always possible. There is no reason to believe that the courts would not accept records or parts that were made several hours after an event occurred; however, the principle must be followed as a guide. A question of admissibility could certainly be raised if entries in the record were made long after the event.

Even if the records that were not made contemporaneously with the facts being recorded were admitted into evidence, the weight or importance given to these records may be seriously damaged. The impression left with the court may be that the person who made the record had a memory lapse between the time the event occurred and the time it was recorded. The greater the amount of time that has elapsed, the greater will be the possibility of its accuracy being questioned.

2. The person making the entry in the record must have "personal knowledge of the matters being recorded". This means that if Nurse A informs Nurse B of a particular fact and Nurse B records that fact, it would not be admissible under the *Ares v. Venner* rule unless Nurse A checked the record. The record of the event could not be placed before the court as evidence that the event actually occurred. The only evidence before the court would be that Nurse A told Nurse B of the fact.

The fact that Nurse A checked Nurse B's record, in addition to the record, becomes a record of the fact as long as Nurse A can testify as to the correctness of the record made by Nurse B. The record is essentially Nurse A's; Nurse B is merely acting as a recorder for Nurse A.

For this reason, it is advisable that those making entries into a health record should only record information, which they personally saw, did, heard or said. Any other matter, which was reported, should be recorded only as having been reported, with the appropriate notation of who reported it. Otherwise the person reporting should check the record and sign accordingly.

3. The only information, which will be admissible under this rule, is that which is recorded by someone who has a duty to make the entry. In an institutional setting a person has such a duty if rules or directives require him or her to make such an entry. Any person who is caring for or treating the individual directly may also be said to have such a duty to make records of that care and treatment whether it is in a health care

---

[4]   14 D.L.R. (3d) 4, at 16 (S.C.C.).

agency, a private office, or at the person's home. Without such records proper care and treatment cannot be given according to a reasonable standard. Therefore, there is a duty to record.

4. The fact that hospital records, including nurses' notes, are admissible under *Ares v. Venner* does not mean that the accuracy of the records will not be questioned. The records are accepted as evidence of certain facts, but the court may not believe that those facts occurred for one reason or another. The facts may also be challenged by having those who recorded the information cross-examined as witnesses.

Prior to the *Ares v. Venner* exception being introduced, with certain minor exceptions only persons who actually saw, did, heard or said something could testify about these events. However, records could be used, and may still be used as an "aide-mémoire" to refresh the present memory of a witness. The witness is not, of course, permitted to recite from the record as if it were a prepared statement.[5]

Chief Justice Gale of the Ontario Court of Appeal stated in *R. v. Gwozdowski*:

> A witness may refresh his memory by reference to any writing made or verified by himself concerning, and contemporaneously with, the facts to which he testifies; but such documents are no evidence *per se* .... [6]

The record, therefore, is not evidence. It is merely to assist the witness in giving his evidence. However, notes can still be admitted into evidence on occasion.[7]

The second method in which the record may be used is as "part memory recorded". In such a case a witness may not remember the information recorded but is able to testify as to its accuracy. The witness states that he prepared the document and that when he prepared it, it was correct, even though he does not currently remember the contents. The record itself is then entered as evidence as was clearly permitted in *Ares v. Venner.*

It is interesting to note that the *Ares v. Venner* decision was in direct contrast to a 1965 decision of the House of Lords in *Myers v. D.P.P.*[8] In that decision a majority of the House of Lords would not make an exception to the hearsay rule and advised that if the law were to be changed, it should be done by Parliament. The Supreme Court of Canada, however, expressly adopted the minority position in the English decision and allowed the hospital records as an exception.

---

5   E. Ratushny, "Basic Problems in Examination and Cross Examination" (1974), 52 C.B.R. 207, at 213.
6   [1973] 2 O.R. 50, 10 C.C.C. (2d) 434, at 437 (C.A.).
7   *Fleming v. Toronto Railways Co.* (1913), 47 S.C.R. 612, 12 D.L.R. 249, 15 C.R.C. 386.
8   [1965] A.C. 1001, [1964] 3 W.L.R. 145.

A number of Canadian provinces followed the advice of the House of Lords and passed legislation allowing hospital records to be admissible as evidence. In those, which did not, the courts were bound by the *Ares v. Venner* ruling.[9] Even in those provinces where legislation has been passed, the *Ares* decision is still cited.

Mr. Justice Richard of the Nova Scotia Supreme Court, Trial Division, based a decision on the *Ares* decision in order to allow into evidence a notation made in medical records with respect to the plaintiff's blood-alcohol level. He then pointed out that even if the Supreme Court of Canada had not found as it did, the medical records would be admissible under Nova Scotia legislation.[10]

THE EXTENT OF ARES v. VENNER

A number of questions arise as to how far *Ares v. Venner* extends. The first is whether it includes not merely the recording of facts, but also the recording of opinions. Nurses' and physicians' opinions are often recorded in health records, and have been questioned as to whether those entries are admissible as evidence.

An opinion may merely be an observation or it may be a judgment. Legal comment seems to suggest that it is not admissible.[11] However, since the records can always be attacked even though they are admitted into evidence, the evidentiary weight could be seriously damaged thus providing a safeguard.

The question must also be raised whether the rule applies *only* to hospitals and to nurses' notes. There is no reason to think that such a restriction would be applied. Records from extended care facilities, clinics, physicians' offices and home care agencies would fall within the same rule.[12]

---

9 See *e.g.*, *Duff v. Brocklehurst* (1978), 20 Nfld. & P.E.I.R. 256, 53 A.P.R. 256, at 260 (Nfld. T.D.).

10 *Cavanaugh v. MacQuarrie* (1979), 9 C.C.L.T. 113, at 121 (N.S.T.D.).

11 J.D. Ewart, "Documentary Evidence: The Admissibility at Common Law of Records Made Pursuant to a Business Duty" (1981), 59 Can. Bar Rev. 1, at 72-73.

12 A number of contrasting cases should also be examined: *Re Maloney* (1971), 5 N.S.R. (2d) 589, 12 R.F.L. 167 (Co. Ct.); *Watkins Products, Inc. v. McDow* (1973), 6 N.S.R. (2d) 49, 36 D.L.R. (3d) 148 (C.A.); *Monsanto Europe S.A. v. Ship "Stolt Atlantic" and Her Owners* (1981), 37 N.R. 543 (F.C.A.).

ADMISSIBILITY BY STATUTE

A number of provinces have passed legislation, which supplants the exception of the hearsay rule in *Ares v. Venner*. The legislation is usually included in a section of evidence legislation relating to business records generally, with a business being defined broadly enough to include hospitals, extended care facilities, clinics, physicians' offices and home care agencies.

A typical example of the type of statute, which permits the admission of records as evidence, is that of Ontario:

> 35(2) Any writing or record made of any act, transaction, occurrence or event is admissible as evidence of such act, transaction, occurrence or event if made in the usual and ordinary course of any business and if it was in the usual and ordinary course of such business to make such writing or record at the time of such act, transaction, occurrence or event or within a reasonable time thereafter.[13]

Similar legislation has been passed in Saskatchewan,[14] Manitoba,[15] New Brunswick,[16] Nova Scotia,[17] British Columbia,[18] Newfoundland and Labrador[19] and Canada under the *Canada Evidence Act*.[20] The question of records of opinion is still open as it can be argued that it would not be included in the categories "act, transaction, occurrence or event". The New Brunswick legislation seems to be more lenient in this regard since it used the words "act, condition or event".[21] The word "condition" could be construed to include medical and nursing opinions as to a condition.

It is interesting to note that some legislation, such as the Ontario *Evidence Act*, has an additional provision that states that the circumstances of the making of such writing or record, including lack of personal knowledge by the maker, may be shown to affect its weight, but such circumstances do not affect its admissibility.[22] The result of this section is that the recording of information which is not directly known by the person recording it, but has merely received a report of it, may be admissible into evidence; however, it may not be believed.

---

[13] *Evidence Act*, R.S.O. 1990, c. E.23, s. 35(2).
[14] S.S. 1978, c. S-16, s. 31.
[15] R.S.M. 1987, c. E150, s. 49(2).
[16] R.S.N.B. 1973, c. E-11, s. 49.
[17] R.S.N.S. 1989, c. 154, s. 23(2).
[18] R.S.B.C. 1996, c. 124, s. 42.
[19] R.S.N.L. 1990, c. E-16, s. 21.
[20] R.S.C. 1985, c. C-5, s. 30.
[21] *Supra*, n. 16.
[22] *Supra*, n. 13, s. 35(4).

MICROFILMED RECORDS AS EVIDENCE

If it was difficult for the courts to accept written documents as evidence of the recorded occurrences, it was even more difficult to accept photographs of the documents. While the written record was one step away from the person who could testify as to his or her personal knowledge of what was recorded, a photograph of a record was two steps away. The first difficulty was overcome by court decisions and legislation.

The second step, that of microfilming, raises the following question: how can the court accept a photograph of the record without knowing whether it is an accurate representation of the record? To overcome this question, legislation specifically addresses the matter allowing courts to accept microfilmed records as evidence in lieu of the original records.[23]

The basic legislation is the same. The general pattern of legislation is similar to that of Nova Scotia[24] with some exceptions.

> 22(1) In this section,
>   (a) "person" includes
>   (i)   the Government of Canada and of any province of Canada and any department, commission, board or branch of any such government,
>   (ii) a corporation,
>   (iii) the heirs, executors, administrators or other legal representatives of a person;
>   (b) "photographic film" includes any photographic plate, microphotographic film and photostatic negative and "photograph" shall have a corresponding meaning.
> (2) Where a bill of exchange, promissory note, cheque, receipt, instrument, agreement, document, plan or a record or book or entry therein kept or held by any person
>   (a) is photographed in the course of an established practice of such person of photographing objects of the same or a similar class in order to keep a permanent record thereof; and
>   (b) is destroyed by or in the presence of the person or of one or more of his employees or delivered to another person in the ordinary course of business or lost,
> a print from the photographic film shall be admissible in evidence in all cases and for all purposes for which the object photographed would have been admissible.

The rule was established: A photograph is admissible in evidence just as the object photographed would have been admissible. The rule applies to all health providers whether institutional or private. It applies to any "record or book" which is broad enough to include health records.

---

[23] See *e.g.*, *Evidence Act*, R.S.N.S. 1989, c. 154; *Evidence Act*, R.S.S. 1978, c. S-16.
[24] *Supra*, n. 23, s. 22.

The definition of "photographic film" includes "microphotographic film" or what is commonly known as microfilm.

For the rule to take effect in any particular situation, the following criteria must be fulfilled:

(1) The microfilming of health records, or a particular part of health records, must be a regular practice. Occasional microfilming will destroy the criteria and remove the applicability of the rule.

(2) The original health record must be either:
   (a) destroyed by or in the presence of the physician or other health provider or his or her employer in the case of health records in his or her office;
   (b) destroyed by or in the presence of an employee of the institution in the case of institutional records;
   (c) delivered to another person (which could include a corporation) in the ordinary course of business; or
   (d) lost.

It is not very difficult to fulfill the criteria. The purpose seems to be to allow the introduction of photographs into court as evidence only if the original records are not available. The only problem therefore, is not in fulfilling the criteria but in proving that the criteria have been met. Documentation must be designed to reflect the fact that these requirements have been met. The signature of the person who has personal knowledge that the requirements have been met should be witnessed and dated. The statement should be made as soon as possible after the destruction, delivery or loss has occurred. Some solicitors prefer the statement to be sworn before a notary public to be acceptable under the legislation.

The type of document required with respect to the photographing of the record would be as follows (similar documents may be drafted for destruction):

I, _____ of _____, in the County of _____, an employee of _____, make oath and say as follows:

1. That films numbered below contain reproductions of documents in the custody of _____ concerning the following:

#	Information re filmed documents	Dates filmed

2. That on the above dates I microfilmed the said documents and certify that they are accurately and completely reproduced on the films as numbered above.

3. That the above listed documents were microfilmed in the course of an established practice of_____in order to keep a permanent record of said documents.

Sworn before me at _____

in the county of _____,

this _____ day of _____ 20   .

_____

A Notary Public in and for the

Province of _____

_____
(Signature)

_____
Name (type or print)

_____
Position (type or print)

While the legislation permitting microfilmed evidence in court is basically the same, attention should be paid to certain jurisdictional differences.

Provincial legislation generally includes exceptions to the rule that photographs of records are admissible. The first is if the original had been destroyed within a period of six years from the time that it was considered current. The second is if the original was destroyed within six years of a notice of any claim by the patient or his family against the health provider.

The exception actually refers to "other executed or signed document" following a list of various commercial documents such as a bill of exchange or promissory note. The question is whether health records are included in the words "other executed or signed document".

Most parts of the health record are in fact signed. Nurses' notes, medical orders and consultations are all signed. The word "executed" simply means something completed[25] or done.[26] At least those parts of the health record, which are signed or otherwise completed, fall into this category.

Assuming therefore that the exception does apply to health records, it would be wise to take administrative steps not to fall within the bounds of the exception. This can be accomplished by establishing a retention period for the original records that is at least six years following the discharge or cessation of treatment or care. In the case of a physician who is permanently providing services to a patient, this minimum period should apply to those parts of the record dealing with matters, which are no longer of current value. Only after this retention period is over should the records be microfilmed and the originals destroyed.

---

[25] *Black's Law Dictionary.*
[26] *Osborn's Concise Law Dictionary.*

However, if notice is received in writing of any claim arising out of the services covered in the records, the file should be specially marked. That file should not be destroyed for six years. The notice need not be the commencement of a lawsuit; it may simply be a letter. Legal advice should be sought on the receipt of such a letter to determine whether it amounts to a notice of a claim as contemplated in the legislation.

This exception, that is the six-year retention requirements of originals, does not apply to governments. Therefore, it would not apply in the case of a hospital or other facility that is a separate corporate entity but is part of a provincial or federal department. In such a case any legal action involving such an institution is brought in the name of the government and not in the name of the institution. In British Columbia and Alberta[27] the exception equally applies to hospital districts.

The retention period for the microfilm should be established in the same way as the retention period for original records since the film is a substitute for the originals. After that period is over the microfilm may be destroyed.

ELECTRONIC RECORDS AS EVIDENCE

If the law had to be amended to accept the use of microfilmed records and to place them on a par with paper records, the advent of electronic transmissions and computer storage created an even greater challenge. Because of the widespread adoption of this means of storing and transmitting information, legislation has been adopted across the country to allow for this. If the existing law required certain information to be in writing, the new legislation allows it to be in electronic form and allows business, including the health business to be carried out in electronic form.[28]

However, as the legislation and regulations under that legislation may not be complete, it is extremely important that careful scrutiny of the existing legislation and regulations allow whatever activity is desired to take place. The legislation and the regulations may not cover all instances. For example, if certain forms or signatures are required, care must be taken to determine if an electronic format may be substituted or

---

[27] *Evidence Act*, R.S.B.C. 1996, c. 124; *Alberta Evidence Act*, R.S.A. 2000, c. A-18.

[28] *Electronic Commerce Act*, S.N.L. 2001, c. E-5.2; *Electronic Commerce Act*, S.P.E.I. 2001, c. 31; *Electronic Transactions Act*, S.N.B. 2001, c. E-5.5; *Electronic Commerce Act*, S.N.S. 2000, c. 26; *An Act to establish a legal framework for information technology*, S.Q. 2001, c. 32; *Electronic Commerce Act*, S.O. 2000, c. 17; *Electronic Commerce & Information Act*, S.M. 2000, c. E-55; *Electronic Information & Documents Act, 2000*, S.S. 2000, c. E-7.22; *Electronic Transactions Act*, S.A. 2001, c. E-6.5; *Electronic Transactions Act*, S.B.C. 2001, c. 10; *Electronic Commerce Act*, S.Y. 2000, c. 10.

whether it is necessary to maintain the information on paper originals. Because the legislative process is continuing, it is imperative that health providers and their legal counsel maintain a constant watch on any changes that may take place in the law. For a more detailed discussion on electronic records as evidence, see Chapter 9 — Computerization and Information Linkage.

USE OF RECORDS AS EVIDENCE

A frequent use of health records in legal proceedings for evidentiary purposes is in civil cases in which one of the parties is a provider of health services and is being accused of negligence. The records are used in an attempt to prove that the provider either did or did not live up to the legally required standard of care. The records may also be used in such a case to provide evidence whether the injuries being complained of were actually suffered or whether the injuries were caused by the alleged negligence of the provider or by someone else.[29]

The records may be used in a case involving a will to determine whether the deceased had the mental capability to have testamentary capacity and thus to determine whether or not the will was valid.[30]

Health records may also be used to show that the plaintiff was partially or totally to blame for the injuries.[31] Similarly, health records may be valuable evidence in criminal trials, divorce cases,[32] labour arbitrations,[33] disciplinary proceedings, child custody cases[34] and personal injury actions.

In any of these situations the position of the parties may be seriously affected by the quality of the records. How they were compiled, what was included in the record and what was omitted may be factors. These factors are quite apart from the effect of the contents of the records as evidence of what did or did not happen.

---

[29] See *e.g.*, *Iler v. Beaudet*, [1971] 3 O.R. 644 (Co. Ct.).

[30] See *e.g.*, *Re Griffin's Estate* (1979), 21 Nfld. & P.E.I.R. 21, 56 A.P.R. 21 (P.E.I.C.A.); motion for leave to appeal to S.C.C. dismissed 24 Nfld. & P.E.I.R. 90*n*, 65 A.P.R. 90*n*.

[31] See *e.g.*, *Cavanaugh v. MacQuarrie, supra*, n. 10.

[32] See discussion in *Geransky v. Geransky* (1979), 13 R.F.L. (2d) 202 (Sask. Q.B.).

[33] See *e.g.*, *Re St. Jean de Brebeuf Hospital v. C.U.P.E., Local 1101* (1977), 16 L.A.C. (2d) 199 (Ont.); *Re Gilbarco Ltd. v. Canadian Union of Golden Triangle Workers* (1973), 5 L.A.C. (2d) 205 (Ont.).

[34] See *e.g.*, *de Genova v. de Genova*, [1971] 3 O.R. 304, 20 D.L.R. (3d) 264, 5 R.F.L. 22 (H.C.J.).

The Route of Health Information
In the Litigation Process

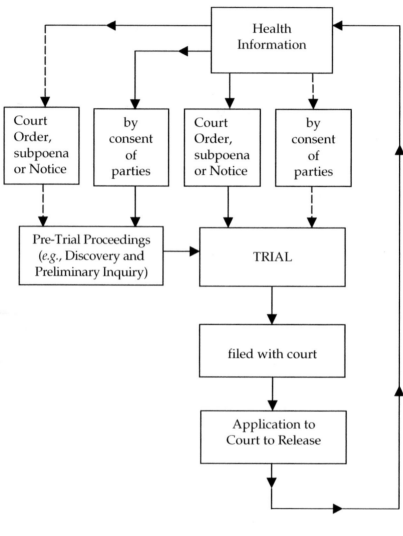

In Kolesar v. Jeffries[35] at the trial level, Mr. Justice Haines of the Ontario High Court said:

> On a ward with a great many patients the medical record becomes the common source of information and direction for patient care. If kept properly it indicates on a regular basis the changes in the patient's condition and alerts staff to developing dangers.... In Kolesar's case the absence of entries permits of the inference that nothing was charted because nothing was done.

It is therefore vitally important that information, which is normally recorded in a health care agency or in a physician's office, must not be omitted. Such a lapse may result in the court inferring that nothing was done, even though the oral testimony may be to the contrary. The court must weigh the record made at the time showing that nothing was done against the memory of the witness in the stressful situation of a trial saying that it was done.

When *Kolesar v. Jeffries* was appealed, the matter of record keeping was commented on further by Mr. Justice Jessup of the Ontario Court of Appeal.[36] His Lordship pointed out that the nurse's failure to record information, which she ordinarily would have recorded, affected her credibility as a witness in testifying on information, which she had not recorded. The law, he said, did not permit him to reverse the trial judge's rejection of her evidence.

When the case was subsequently heard by the Supreme Court of Canada, the principle was confirmed that it is not the function of the appellate court to reconsider the evidence whether it be upon facts or a matter of professional opinion and come to a different conclusion, unless it could be shown that evidence could not reasonably result in justifying the conclusion made by the trial judge.[37]

The failure to chart necessary information is often the centrepiece of negligence litigation. Indeed, gaps in the record may actually trigger litigation,[38] and in some cases it may actually lead to or contribute to staff

---

[35] (1974), 9 O.R. (2d) 41, 59 D.L.R. (3d) 367, at 373 (H.C.).

[36] (1976), 12 O.R. (2d) 142, 68 D.L.R. (3d) 198, at 208 (C.A.).

[37] [1978] 1 S.C.R. 491, 77 D.L.R. (3d) 161, 2 C.C.L.T. 170, at 182 *per* Spence J.

[38] See *e.g.*, *Pike v. Peace Arch District Hospital Society* (1985), 33 A.C.W.S. (2d) 490 (B.C.S.C.), in which the judge concluded his opinion by noting,

> Since I believe it [the lawsuit] would not have been brought had the defendants maintained complete and regular records of vital signs and of other important observations, in accordance with proper hospital practice, I find it inappropriate that costs should be awarded in their favour.

Refusing to award costs in favour of the defence was one way the judge could use the "judicial process" to bring home the message of appropriate record keeping as being an expected standard of care.

privileges action.[39] Such was the case in a British Columbia situation in which a physician appealed a hospital board's decision to revoke his staff privileges. The doctor, an orthopaedic surgeon, had experienced previous suspensions of staff privileges. While on probation, the doctor saw two individuals in the emergency department in December 1990 resulting in the hospital receiving complaints of unreasonable delays in treatment. An independent audit was conducted by an orthopaedist who concluded that care was substandard in only one of the cases. Further, the hospital claimed that with regard to the remaining case, the doctor concocted an explanation and documentation to demonstrate an appropriate level of care.

Late in the afternoon of December 5, 1990, an individual had severely lacerated his fingers with a table saw. The injury was so severe that he had amputated the index finger. The man was referred to Dr. Hicks and, after examining him, the doctor scheduled him for surgery the next afternoon. Throughout the following day the man became increasingly agitated because of the delay. The vice-president for medical services of the hospital was summoned to speak with him. He apparently calmed down after speaking at length with another staff orthopaedist. Surgery was performed during the evening of December 6 and was relatively successful.

Dr. Hicks claimed that the delay was occasioned by a switch of the man's case with that of another individual on the O.R. schedule. The independent evaluator claimed that the doctor's conduct was substandard. He based his opinion on a review of the individual's chart as well as his x-rays. In particular, he took exception to the fact that there was no evidence in the record that the wound was debrided in the emergency department. Dr. Hicks claimed that he had performed a wound debridement and produced his copy of the emergency room form as "evidence" to this effect. He claimed on the back of the form there was reference to an emergency room debridement and a notation "LOC" signifying that a local anaesthetic had been administered. He claimed that he had taken the document home with him and had given it to his billing clerk. Aside from time discrepancies on the doctor's emergency room sheet, there were other factors, which cast doubt on the credibility of the notation. First, the doctor called a health record analyst at the hospital that took notes of their conversation. Prior to the hearing the doctor asked her, "Did we do debridement and what was ordered?"[40] Further, the doctor's billing clerk stated that he did not give her the E.R. form until December 10, and that she never looked at the back of the documents for purposes

---

[39]   See, *In the Matter of the Hospital Act and Hospital Act Regulations of B.C.* (unreported decision of the B.C. Medical Appeal Board, June, 1991).

[40]   *Ibid.*, at 17.

of billing. This was in direct contravention of the doctor's claim that he made notes on the back of E.R. forms for billing purposes.

Given the inconsistencies in the doctor's records and evidence, the medical appeal board concluded that it was difficult to accept the claim that a wound debridement had been performed in the emergency room. It castigated the hospital for what it described as "atrocious" record keeping. The medical appeal board accepted the hospital's concern that the doctor concocted an explanation to cover for an unacceptable delay in care. In the end the medical appeal board upheld the hospital's decision to revoke the doctor's privileges.

Leaving out necessary or required information is a serious flaw in contemporary health care. "Gaps" in health record keeping can be a signal or "red flag" to a plaintiff's solicitor pointing to possible substandard care. In the case of medical staff physicians, dentists and psychologists, unacceptable charting practices can be the basis for privileges action. It could also lead to licensure actions. It is not a matter to be taken lightly.

The British Columbia case also illustrates another important point. Health records must be consistent with institutional or agency charting policies and procedures. It is not up to an individual health care provider to "change" the system. Charting on the back of a form rather than the front as a matter of personal convenience is unacceptable. Refraining from noting treatment or observations because "nothing has changed" is equally unacceptable. Courts and disciplinary bodies are entitled to draw inferences from such behaviour that may be contrary to the interests of the professional or health care agency. As such, these practices should be discouraged.

The effect on evidentiary value of leaving out information from the record is equalled by the effect of changes that may be made in the record. In *Meyer v. Gordon*[41] entries in the records were made in different coloured inks and contained alterations in the figures. It was admitted that the entries were completed sometime after they were first made. The result was the loss of credibility of the evidence. The unreliability not only affects the proof of the facts contained in the records, it also affects the opinions of the expert witnesses which are based on the records. The conclusion in that case was summed up by Mr. Justice Legg in his judgment:

> The accuracy of Dr. Ueland's opinion and the weight which I should attach to it, depends in large measure on the accuracy of the nursing observations and the nurses' charting ... I have found that these observations are not reliable. I am therefore unable to accept Dr. Ueland's opinion based upon them.[42]

---

[41] (1981), 17 C.C.L.T. 1 (B.C.S.C.).
[42] *Ibid.*, at 25.

In a more recent case, a doctor was held negligent for a needle lodged in a patient's lung.[43] The patient had undergone a hernia operation. During the procedure a needle count revealed that an eyed needle was missing. A search for the needle proved unsuccessful and an x-ray was taken. The needle was not found and the operation proceeded.

The patient was never told about the retained needle. During a series of x-rays four years later an eyed needle was found in his left lung. A decision was made to leave the needle undisturbed unless the patient encountered difficulties from it.

In a lawsuit that followed, the surgeon was held negligent. Disturbing evidence emerged, which may have in part precipitated the Court's ruling. The Court found that the intra-operative x-ray report completed by the radiologist on the day of the hernia surgery suggested that a "chest x-ray" of the patient had been taken. However, the radiologist amended this to read "abdomen" *after* the patient launched his lawsuit. To compound matters, the x-ray could not be produced at trial because it had been retained by the hospital.

The *Vyse* case illustrates the importance of having an appropriate procedure for altering information in health care records. Changes made after litigation has been commenced are likely to be suspect. Judges are entitled to draw the inference that subsequent changes are intended to put the defendant in a better light. If the change is unusual or does not adhere to a set practice for handling latent information, the modified entry could damage the credibility of the record as well as the testimony given by relevant witnesses. The better practice is to develop a practical procedure for handling modifications to records, which does not call into question the credibility of the documentation as evidence for the defence.

PRIVILEGED DOCUMENTS

The law has always recognized that there are certain situations in which information and communication should not be divulged. Ordinarily the principle is that the justice system can only function to the benefit of all if whatever is necessary for the proceedings is made known. However, there are a number of situations, which have developed whereby the importance of secrecy overrides the value of making the facts known.

Under common law, three kinds of communication between private persons have been generally recognized as privileged. They are communications between solicitor and client, communications between spouses,

---

[43] See *Vyse v. The Sisters of St. Joseph & Sweeney* (July 11, 1990), Doc. No. 4939/86 (Ont. Dist. Ct.).

and communications made without prejudice with a view to achieving the settlement of matters in litigation. By common law, health records do not fall within any of these categories. They are not privileged and ordinarily can be divulged in court without the individual's consent.

It should be noted that in Quebec a physician who appears as a witness in court is not obliged to divulge information which has been given to him in confidence by the individual.[44] No witness is required to answer questions in court if the answer will subject him to legal proceedings.[45]

In addition, some provinces, including the Northwest Territories, have statutory provisions, which create a privilege under certain circumstances.[46] Although most of these statutory privileges are found in evidence acts, there are exceptions. Prince Edward Island is a good illustration. Statutory privilege is found not in the *Evidence Act*,[47] but in the provincial *Medical Act*.[48] Privilege is granted to members of a medical audit committee, quality assurance committee, or similar group in a hospital in Prince Edward Island as well as committees of the provincial medical society and College of Physicians and Surgeons.[49]

The wording of these sections must be considered carefully in light of the circumstances in each case. These provisions do not create a privilege in all circumstances. It does not mean that health records that go before such a committee cannot be subject to production in legal proceedings. It would be a matter of whether what is being sought fell clearly within the categories mentioned in the legislation.

The same cautionary note applies to the privileges granted in evidence legislation found in other jurisdictions. The language of the law must be read very carefully to determine the scope of its coverage. In some instances, protection extends beyond hospitals to include other services. The expanse of protection is quite clear. For example, in the Northwest Territories, "hospitals" includes nursing stations, health centres, nursing homes and the coordinated home care program,[50] and in Newfoundland and Labrador, coverage extends to the quality assurance

---

[44] *Charter of Human Rights and Freedoms*, s. 9, Part I of the *Constitution Act, 1982*, being Schedule B to the *Canada Act 1982* (U.K.), 1982, c. 11.

[45] *Code of Civil Procedure*, R.S.Q. 1977, c. C-25, s. 309.

[46] See, for example, *Manitoba Evidence Act*, R.S.M. 1987, c. E150, ss. 8, 9; British Columbia *Evidence Act*, R.S.B.C. 1996, c. 124, s. 57; New Brunswick *Evidence Act*, S.N.B. 1973, c. E-11, s. 43(1)-(4); Nova Scotia *Evidence Act*, R.S.N.S. 1989, c. 154, ss. 60-61; Newfoundland and Labrador *Evidence Act*, R.S.N. 1990, c. E-16, s. 6.1; *Saskatchewan Evidence Act*, R.S.S. 1978, c. S-16, s. 35 and Northwest Territories *Evidence Act*, R.S.N.W.T. 1988, c. E-8, ss. 13-15.

[47] R.S.P.E.I. 1988, c. E-11.

[48] *Medical Act*, R.S.P.E.I. 1988, c. M-5, s. 52.

[49] *Ibid.*

[50] Northwest Territories *Evidence Act*, *supra*, n. 46, s. 13.

and peer review committees of member organizations defined under the *Health Care Association Act* (formerly *Hospital and Nursing Home Association Act*).[51]

The extent of privilege granted is not only dependent upon the type of health care agency mentioned in the legislation, it also depends on the type of proceedings, documentation, and witnesses specified in the law. For example, the Nova Scotia *Evidence Act* deals with hospital-based research committees, hospital committees that study and evaluate medical or hospital care or hospital-based practice, and research committees approved by the Minister of Health and Fitness for purposes of the Act.[52] The law goes on to give further precision to the scope of coverage, noting that a witness in any legal proceeding is excused from answering questions about proceedings before or producing documentation made by the committees described earlier where this information

> ... is used in the course of, or arising out of, any study, research or program carried on by a hospital or any such committee for the purpose of education or improvement in medical or hospital care or practice.[53]

The extent of coverage and exceptions under these laws is sometimes more straightforward in one jurisdiction than another. This is true in Newfoundland and Labrador where the privilege accorded under the *Evidence Act* is sweeping yet written in very concise, easy-to-read language[54] and in the British Columbia *Evidence Act* with its delineated lists of organizations, health care professionals and legal proceedings covered under the law.[55] In many cases, however, the "privilege" found in legislation does require careful interpretation.

To determine what is and what is not "covered" is an important issue for all health care agencies and professionals. Where legislation grants privilege to "research" or "quality assurance" committees, it may be prudent to make certain that either the name or mandate of these committees specifies that it fulfills the intent of the legislation in order to avoid lengthy legal battles of interpretation. Such concerns could be avoided in the first instance if health care agencies and professionals secured legal advice from lawyers trained in health law. For a discussion on Privilege and Incident Reports, see Chapter 17 — Risk Management in Health Information.

---

[51] R.S.N.L. 1990, c. H-8, s. 4.

[52] *Supra*, n. 46, s. 60(2).

[53] *Ibid.*, s. 60(2).

[54] *Supra*, n. 46, s. 6.1(3). Indeed, a good case could be made under the law that incident reports are protected under the privilege found in this section.

[55] R.S.B.C. 1996, c. 124, s. 51.

The issue of records as evidence and the scope of privilege is bound to take on more significance with increased interest among health care agencies and professional groups in scrutinizing treatment practices. Peer review has taken on added significance in light of concern about possible corporate liability. Similarly, concerns stemming from quality and utilization management have engendered a need for detailed review of professional practice that extends beyond physicians. This is well illustrated by changes expected in Ontario under the new Regulated Health Professions legislation.[56]

The legislative privilege issue is a good illustration of the need to protect the public and to enable a litigant to have fair access to information on the one hand, and on the other, the concomitant concerns of health care agencies to conduct frank and detailed review of treatment practices. It remains to be seen whether a new body of case law will emerge in Canada in which the courts will hammer out the fine details of this delicate balance. What may tip the balance is a demonstrated failure on the part of health care agencies and professional groups to discharge their duties in terms of overseeing quality of care and fulfilling peer review tasks. If quality care is not maintained or improved, or peer review mechanisms fail to weed out unacceptable health care providers, the incentive for protective legislation may be lost. A loss of the privilege granted in legislation could follow.

Despite the fact that the common law does not consider client-physician communications as being privileged, medical testimony has on occasion been excluded. Its exclusion is at the discretion of the judge, leading one to the conclusion that health records, whether from an institution or at a private physician's office, are essentially available to the courts unless the discretion is exercised. The onus of showing that it should be exercised would be on the party opposing its disclosure.

It must therefore be concluded that the standard hospital and medical record is usually discoverable unless a specific statutory provision provides to the contrary or judicial discretion is exercised.

---

[56] *Regulated Health Professions Act, 1991*, S.O. 1991, c. 18.

7

Access to Health Information

ISSUES

Traditionally health facilities and providers have been reluctant to provide access to health records to individuals. In the past, access to health information has been viewed as the exclusive purview of health providers. In support of this position, health information is documented for purposes of communication among health personnel not for purposes of disclosure to the subject of the health information.

Health information is written in clinical terminology, which is not easily understood and could be misleading to the individual. There is concern that health information could have a detrimental effect on some individuals such as psychiatric patients. Verbal communication of health information enables staff to provide an explanation. However, the view that only health providers know what is best for patients and have exclusive access to health information is a view of the past.

There are many reasons supporting the right of access by individuals to their own health information. Individuals require access to information to understand their health and to make appropriate treatment and life style decisions. Individuals have the right to consent or refuse consent to treatment and for disclosure of health information to third parties. The growth of access to information requests has accompanied a growth in consumer rights associations and access trends in provincial legislation and court decisions[1] that require more communication of health information to individuals.

Some health agencies not only encourage individuals to read and understand their health information, but also to do some of their own charting. Self-charting by patients, home care clients and other recipients of care has limitations such as possible inaccuracy and irrelevant information. However, the individual's perception is a valid observation that provides insights otherwise unavailable to health personnel. Criticism of staff entries may provide an early warning of difficulties between recipients of care and health providers.

---

[1] See *e.g.*, *Reibl v. Hughes*, [1980] 2 S.C.R. 880, 114 D.L.R. (3d) 1, 33 N.R. 361, 14 C.C.L.T. 1.

Health providers may be concerned about access to records containing extremely sensitive health information. With the burgeoning field of community health care and increased emphasis on areas such as detoxification and drug treatment and mental health centres, there is an ever-increasing amount of extremely sensitive health information. Sensitive health information relating to continuing competence, performance appraisal, practice review, quality improvement and risk management may also create concerns about access.

Health providers may be reluctant to record "sensitive" information with impressions, conjecture and opinions, which is subject to access requests. Some providers believe that client access to candid written observations will create distrust that will seriously damage the therapeutic relationship. This highly sensitive information may be recorded but kept separate from the main health record in a secret file. There are dangers in this approach. The absence of salient information could lead subsequent caregivers to provide inappropriate treatment. If the elements of a negligence lawsuit exist, this could mean successful litigation.

Keeping secret files could breach the professional duty to keep an accurate and complete health record, with serious repercussions.[2] Specific health records may be required for programs such as drug detoxification[3] or community mental health. Some concerns are addressed in legislative exceptions to the right of access. For example, the Nova Scotia Commission on Drug Dependency can refuse to release details from an individual's record where the Commission "has reasonable grounds to believe it would not be in the best interest of the person to make available that information"[4]

From a practical perspective, access issues can be minimized with an open and honest approach. Particularly where highly sensitive information is involved, it is reasonable to inform individuals of the information that will be documented. As the therapeutic relationship is nurtured, it is more likely that the need for surreptitious record keeping will not exist.

Another concern relating to access is preserving integrity and avoiding loss or alteration of health information. Home care agencies may leave health information in the client's home rather than transport it back and forth. The agency could encourage the client to read the home care record. The record should be in a secure place to discourage viewing by unauthorized individuals.

Firm ground rules should govern record access. However, an "agreement" between the client and the caregiver to place the record in a secure

---

[2] J.H. Haydon, "Legal Aspects of Health Information" in *Health Law in Canada*, vol. 21, no. 2, November 1999, at 1-8.

[3] See *e.g.*, *Drug Dependency Act*, R.S.N.S. 1989, c. 133.

[4] *Ibid.*, s. 10(3).

place in the home is no guarantee that it will be safe. If a decision is made to store the record in the client's home, the agency must assess the risk involved. The opportunity may be great for damage, destruction, loss and alteration. Rules are of little value if the client or the client's caregiver suffer short-term memory loss and cannot recall what they did with the record.

A practical solution may be to keep most of the information at the office and selectively keep some information in the home. Some information such as reminders on the fridge may be essential for the client to manage. If health information is kept in the client's home, important details such as the home care plan, alerts and special instructions should be maintained in duplicate so if the home copy is misplaced it is possible to maintain continuity of service.

Electronic health records may resolve some of these problems as caregivers can readily transport palm pilots and laptop computers from the office to the home. However, these devices raise other issues such as the security of electronic health information. (See Chapter 9 – Computerization and Information Linkage.)

OWNERSHIP

Any discussion of client access to health information invariably raises the subject of ownership of the records. The issue of ownership of health information has been addressed in legislation by legal authorities and by the courts.

Legislation in Ontario in the *Public Hospitals Act* says that "the medical record compiled in a hospital for a patient or an out-patient is the property of the hospital".[5] Enactments in British Columbia,[6] Newfoundland and Labrador[7] and Saskatchewan[8] recognize hospital ownership of health records. In the Northwest Territories, inpatient and outpatient medical records are the property of the hospital.[9] Even where provincial legislation does not specifically address ownership, health agencies clearly have a proprietary role to maintain records, chart specific information and provide access to health information.[10]

---

[5]   R.S.O. 1990, c. P. 40, s. 14.
[6]   *Hospital Act*, R.S.B.C. 1979, c. 176, s. 43(1), as am. 1983, c. 20, s. 21.
[7]   *Hospitals Act*, R.S.N.L. 1990, c. H-9, s. 35(1).
[8]   Sask. Reg. 331/79, s. 16(1).
[9]   R.R.N.W.T. 1980, Reg. 275, s. 75(1).
[10] See *e.g.*, R.R.O. 1980, Reg. 690, ss. 87-89, under the *Nursing Homes Act*, R.S.O. 1990, c. N.7.

Legal authorities[11] as well as the courts[12] have adopted the principle that the physical property in the health record (*i.e.*, the paper, film, videotape or tape) belongs to the health agency that compiled the record. This principle is illustrated in the case of *Lamothe v. Mokleby*[13] where it was determined that the owner of a dental practice is also the owner of the dental records. This principle applies to all health facilities and providers, including nursing homes, mental health centres, outpatient clinics and laboratories.

Ownership of the physical property in health information should not be confused with the right of access by individuals to their health information. The right of access is a qualified right of individuals to inspect and copy their own health information. The right of individuals to their health information is not based upon a proprietary right of ownership, but upon the fiduciary duty of health providers to patients.

The issue of whether a patient medical record prepared by a physician is the property of the physician or the patient was authoritatively addressed at common law in 1992 by the Supreme Court of Canada in *McInerney v. MacDonald*.[14] In *McInerney*, a patient asked her doctor for a copy of her complete office medical file. The file involved advice to stop taking thyroid pills that earlier doctors had prescribed. Dr. McInerney provided all her notations but refused to provide consultant reports and records from five other physicians.

The Supreme Court of Canada dismissed the appeal, meaning that the doctor had to provide a copy of the entire medical file to the patient. This case arose in New Brunswick where there is no legislation on this issue. The Court said that in the absence of legislation, a patient is entitled to examine and copy all information in the medical record that a physician considered in providing the treatment, including records prepared by others. The Court held that the patient had a "vital interest"[15] in the information and that the right of access arose within the fiduciary relationship between physician and patient.

The right of access is not absolute and can be denied where a health provider can show a paramount reason that overrides this right, such as

---

[11] E. Picard and G. Robertson, *Legal Liability of Doctors and Hospitals in Canada*, 3rd ed. (Toronto: Carswell, 1996), at 406; M. Litman and G. Robertson, "The Common Law Status of Genetic Material" in B. Knoppers, T. Caulfield, and D. Kinsella, *Legal Rights and Human Genetic Material* (Toronto: Emond Montgomery, 1996), at 58-59; B. Dickens, "Medical Records — Patient's Right to Receive Copies — Physician's Fiduciary Duty of Disclosure: *McInerney v. MacDonald*" (1994), 73 Can. Bar Rev. 234, at 237.

[12] *Halls v. Mitchell*, [1928] S.C.R. 125; *Mellen v. Nelligan and St. Mary's Hospital*, [1952] Que. S.C. 446; *C. v. C.*, [1946] 1 All E.R. 562; *Selkirk v. Hyde and Royal Victoria Hospital*, [1958] R.P. 281; *R. v. Stewart* (1988), 50 D.L.R. (4th) 1, at 10 (S.C.C.).

[13] *Lamothe v. Mokleby* (1979), 4 Sask. R. 352, 106 D.L.R. (3d) 233 (Q.B.).

[14] *McInerney v. MacDonald*, [1992] 2 S.C.R. 138, 93 D.L.R. (4th) 415.

[15] *Ibid.*, at 144 (S.C.C.).

harm to the individual or others. The Court held that the patient was not entitled to the records themselves, as the physical or medical records belonged to the physician. In regards to individual access, the Court said:

> The physician-patient relationship is fiduciary in nature and certain duties arise from that special relationship of trust and confidence. These include the duties of the doctor to act with utmost good faith and loyalty, to hold information received from or about a patient in confidence, and to make proper disclosure of information to the patient. The doctor also has an obligation to grant access to the information used in administering treatment. This fiduciary duty is ultimately grounded in the nature of the patient's interest in the medical records. Information about oneself revealed to a doctor acting in a professional capacity remains, in a fundamental sense, one's own. While the doctor is the owner of the actual record, the information is held in a fashion somewhat akin to a trust...[16]

Therefore, although the health provider or facility owns the tangible physical record, the individual has a right to the health information.

COMMON LAW

The courts have occasionally reviewed the legislation authorizing individual access to health information so there are some judicial decisions or common law on the issue of individual access. However, it is difficult to generalize principles from the common law since the court decisions are usually based on a particular statute.

In 1981 the Alberta Court of Appeal dealt with client access under the *Mental Health Act*[17] in *Lindsay v. M. (D.)*.[18] A psychiatric patient was denied access to hospital records for an involuntary commitment. The Court ordered the facility to provide a copy of the information to the patient. The Court said the legislation gave the individual a right of access, which will not be removed by the Court unless there is a compelling reason.

In Ontario, the regulations under the *Public Hospitals Act* and the *Independent Health Facilities Act* authorize hospitals to release the records to patients.[19] When considering the same enactment, one Ontario court re-

---

[16] *Ibid.*, at 139 (S.C.R.).

[17] Then *Mental Health Act*, S.A. 1972, c. 118, s. 50.1 (now R.S.A. 2000, but section since repealed).

[18] [1981] 3 W.W.R. 703, 121 D.L.R. (3d) 261 (Alta. C.A.).

[19] R.R.O. 1990, Reg. 965, s. 22(6)(c); O. Reg. 57/92, s. 12(2), as am. O. Reg. 14/95, s. 1(1)-(6).

quired a hospital to provide access to health records[20] while another Ontario court took the opposite view and did not require a hospital to provide access without litigation.[21]

Access to health information can usually be compelled in legal proceedings or by court order under provincial or territorial Rules of Court
or Rules of Practice once litigation has begun. Lawsuits have been commenced merely to obtain access to health records.[22] Judicial decisions
vary depending upon the specific provisions in the various Rules of
Court. The Manitoba Court of Queen's Bench did not order a hospital to
provide access in *Andree v. Misericordia General Hospital*[23] as the rules of
court in Manitoba do not provide specific direction on access to health
records.

In the British Columbia case of *Bachmann v. Sandoz (Canada) Ltd.*[24] the
Court found that the Supreme Court Rules allowed access to health records and ordered the hospital to provide access. Mr. Justice Trainor stated:

> In my opinion the hospitals are obliged to disclose to the plaintiff all of
> the information about him in their records. Those records are their
> property but the plaintiff is entitled to know what is in them and to use
> that information. For that purpose he is entitled to see the records and
> to make copies of them. This is the reasonable arrangement which
> ought to be made rather than resorting to other avenues such as a sub-
> poena duces tecum at trial or a pre-trial examination of a witness....[25]

The general conclusion is that a person taking legal action against a
health provider can usually obtain access to health information under the
various provincial civil procedure rules.

The further question is whether an individual has the right of access
without taking legal action against the owner of the record. Recent developments indicate a trend toward individuals having a right of access
without resorting to litigation. This new right of access is based upon a
number of recent developments that have arisen in the common law, in
professional codes and in legislation.

The Supreme Court of Canada in *McInerney* clearly indicated that individuals have a right of access to their health information, even without
provincial legislation. With regard to the patient's right of access Justice
La Forest stated:

[20] *Strazdins v. Orthopaedic & Arthritic Hospital* (1978), 22 O.R. (2d) 47, 7 C.P.C. 243, 7 C.C.L.T.
      117 (H.C.).
[21] *Mitchell v. St. Michael's Hospital* (1980), 29 O.R. (2d) 185, 112 D.L.R. (3d) 360, 19 C.P.C.
      113 (H.C.).
[22] *Sugrue v. Brown* (1979), 14 C.P.C. 114 (Ont. Master). Also see *Millward v. Reid* (1981), 2
      C.P.C. 101 (Ont. Div. Ct.).
[23] [1980] 2 W.W.R. 380, 107 D.L.R. (3d) 696, 15 C.P.C. 239 (Man. Q.B.).
[24] (1978), 6 B.C.L.R. 57 (S.C.).
[25] *Ibid.*, at 65.

> I find it unnecessary to reify the patient's interest in his or her medical records and, in particular, I am not inclined to go so far as to say that a doctor is merely a "custodian" of medical information. The fiduciary duty I have described is sufficient to protect the interest of the patient. The trust-like "beneficial interest" of the patient in the information indicates that, as a general rule, he or she should have a right of access to the information and that the physician should have a corresponding obligation to provide it. The patient's interest being in the information, it follows that the interest continues when that information is conveyed to another doctor who then becomes subject to the duty to afford the patient access to that information.[26]

The basis for individual access at common law is the fiduciary relationship of trust and confidence between the health provider and the patient.

Professional Codes have also indicated that individuals have a right of access without resorting to litigation. The Canadian Health Record Association's (CHRA) "Position Statement on Patient Access to Health Records" is a useful tool for health agencies dealing with access requests. A further example is the Canadian Medical Association Health Information Privacy Code,[27] which was approved in 1998 and says:

> Principle 6 — Individual Access — Patients have the right of access to their health information. In rare and limited circumstances, health information may be withheld from a patient if there is a significant likelihood of a substantial adverse effect on the physical, mental or emotional health of the patient or substantial harm to a third party. The onus lies on the provider to justify a denial of access.[28]

The CMA Code has been adopted by various medical associations across Canada and has been widely discussed in regards to access and privacy of health information.

HEALTH SECTOR LEGISLATION

The provinces and territories have historically passed health sector legislation that gives individuals a limited right of access to health information. The legislation may provide exceptions to this right and a procedure for individuals to enforce the right when denied. This type of legislation applies only to specific facilities such as hospitals, mental health facilities, cancer programs, home care programs, long term care facilities and public health centres but not to private health agencies.

---

[26] *Supra*, n. 14, at 152.
[27] Canadian Medical Association Health Information Privacy Code, approved August 15, 1998.
[28] *Ibid.*, Principle 6, at 20.

In some provinces and territories, the authority to provide access exists in health sector regulations. In the Yukon[29] and the Northwest Territories[30] regulations provide authority for patients to receive hospital records. In Alberta, the *Confidentiality Regulation*[31] under the *Ambulance Services Act* allows an ambulance operator to disclose health information to a patient. Similarly, in New Brunswick[32] and Prince Edward Island[33] regulations provide authority to disclose health information to patients.

In British Columbia, a regulation allows the board to provide an original x-ray to the patient.[34] A Saskatchewan regulation permits access to hospital records and says that the records "shall be disclosed" upon a court order.[35] Prince Edward Island[36] has a similar regulation that applies to hospitals.

In other jurisdictions, access to health information is governed by statute. For example, the *Hospitals Act* of Nova Scotia permits patient access to health records but allows a hospital or physician to refuse "if he has reasonable grounds to believe it would not be in the best interest of the patient to make available that information".[37] An appeal of the hospital decision can be made to the court in Nova Scotia. Similarly, the *Hospitals Act* in Newfoundland and Labrador creates authority for patient access to hospital records.[38]

In Quebec, *An Act Respecting Health Services and Social Services* provides access to health records in "establishments".[39] Establishments mean a local community service centre, a hospital centre, a social service centre or a reception centre.[40] The Quebec legislation also gives the individual the option of seeking access to health records by application to the Commission d'accès à l'information.[41]

Special attention should be paid to provincial mental health legislation, which governs psychiatric hospitals as distinct from general or public hospitals. All provinces have special legislation governing psychiatric hospitals except Nova Scotia. In Nova Scotia the *Hospitals Act* governs all hospitals whether public or psychiatric. The procedure for obtaining client access to records in a psychiatric hospital in Nova Scotia is the same as in any other hospital.[42]

---

[29] Y.T.O.I.C. 1994/227, s. 11(6)(c)(i).
[30] R.R.N.W.T. 1990, c. T-6, s. 74(1)(c).
[31] Alta. Reg. 38/99, s. 4(a).
[32] N.B. Reg. 92-94, s. 21(1)(d).
[33] P.E.I. *Hospital Management Regulations*, EC 574/76, s. 47(5)(c)(i).
[34] B.C. Reg. 289/73, s. 14.1.
[35] Sask. Reg. 331/79, s. 16(1)(2).
[36] *Supra*, n. 33, s. 47(5).
[37] R.S.N.S. 1989, c. 208, s. 71(1)-(3).
[38] R.S.N.L. 1990, c. H-9, s. 35(3)(a).
[39] R.S.Q. 1977, c. S-5, s. 7.
[40] *Ibid.*, s. 1(a).
[41] *Ibid.*, s. 7.
[42] *Supra*, n. 37.

The Ontario *Mental Health Act*[43] restricts access to psychiatric records. A mentally competent individual is entitled to see or copy the health record and may make a written request. Upon the advice of the attending physician, the officer in charge may apply to the review board for authority to withhold all or part of the health record. The hospital board must permit access to the health record unless it is of the opinion that disclosure is likely to result in:

(a) serious harm to the treatment or recovery of the person while in treatment at the psychiatric facility; or

(b) serious physical harm or serious emotional harm to another person.[44]

The question arises whether individuals have a right of access in facilities that are without health sector legislation.

FREEDOM OF INFORMATION LEGISLATION

All Canadian jurisdictions now have legislative provisions governing access to personal information, which may specifically include health information. A few jurisdictions have health information legislation that creates a right of access to health information.

Provincial freedom of information and protection of privacy legislation is often referred to as "FOIP" legislation, which covers access to (freedom of) information as well as protection of privacy. All federal,[45] provincial[46] and territorial[47] jurisdictions in Canada have now enacted

[43] R.S.O. 1990, c. M.7.

[44] *Ibid.*

[45] *Access to Information Act*, R.S.C. 1985, c. A-1; *Privacy Act*, R.S.C. 1985, c. P-21.

[46] *Freedom of Information and Protection of Privacy Act*, R.S.B.C. 1996, c. 165; *Protection of Personal Information Act*, S.N.B. 2001, c. P-19.1, proclaimed April 2001; *Freedom of Information Act*, R.S.N. 1990, c. F-25, rep. and sub. S.N.L. 2002, c. A-1.1 (not yet in force); *Privacy Act*, R.S.N.L. 1990, c. P-22; *Freedom of Information and Protection of Privacy Act*, S.N.S. 1993, c. 5; *Freedom of Information and Protection of Privacy Act*, R.S.O. 1990, c. F. 31; *Municipal Freedom of Information and Protection of Privacy Act*, R.S.O. 1990, c. M-56; *Freedom of Information and Protection of Privacy Act, (No. 2)*, S.P.E.I. 2001, c. 37 (Bill 47); Royal Assent on May 15, 2001, not yet proclaimed; *Act Respecting Access to Documents held by Public Bodies and the Protection of Personal Information*, R.S.Q. 1993, c. A-2.1, Enacted June 22, 1982; *Freedom of Information and Protection of Privacy Act*, S.S. 1990-91, c. F-22.01; *Local Authority Freedom of Information and Protection of Privacy Act*, S.S. 1990-91, c. L-27.1 (also refer to An Inside Look at the Office of the Information and Privacy Commissioner, Health Law Seminars, LESA, April 2002, at 6-7).

[47] *Access to Information and Protection of Privacy Act (Nunavut)*, S.N.W.T. 1994, c. 20 (Nunavut enacted under s. 76.05 of *Nunavut Act*); *Access to Information and Protection of Privacy Act*, S.N.W.T. 1994, c. 20; *Access to Information and Protection of Privacy Act*, S.Y. 1995, c. 1.

FOIP legislation. Prince Edward Island and Newfoundland and Labrador are the only jurisdictions that have not yet proclaimed FOIP legislation. FOIP legislation typically covers the public sector and creates a statutory right to access information held by public bodies. Individuals have a right of access to their own personal information with certain exceptions.

An access provision that exists in the provincial FOIP legislation in British Columbia is as follows:

> 4(1) A person who makes a request under section 5 has a right of access to any record in the custody or under the control of a public body, including a record containing personal information about the applicant.
> (2) The right of access to a record does not extend to information excepted from disclosure under Division 2 of this Part, but if that information can reasonably be severed from a record an applicant has the right of access to the remainder of the record.[48]

Exceptions to the statutory right of access are listed in Division 2 and include disclosures that are harmful to individual or public safety or to personal privacy.[49]

Under the British Columbia FOIP legislation, information that relates to abortion services must not be disclosed unless the services were received by the applicant.[50] The British Columbia legislation applies to publicly funded health sector bodies including workers compensation and professional regulatory bodies.[51] The B.C. Commissioner recently denied an access request on the basis of a threat to safety.[52]

An access request for practice review information was partially denied in a recent decision of the Review Officer in Nova Scotia,[53] Barring limited exceptions, FOIP legislation creates a clear right of access by individuals to their own personal information. The body denying access must satisfy the burden of proof to justify refusal of access.

Private sector legislation governs access to personal information held by the private sector. Private sector freedom of information legislation has existed for some time in the province of Quebec.[54] Personal information held by an organization that conducts commercial activities is now governed at the federal level by the *Personal Information Protection and*

---

[48] *Freedom of Information and Protection of Privacy Act*, R.S.B.C. 1996, c. 165, s. 4(1)-(2).
[49] *Ibid.*, Division 2, ss. 12-22.1.
[50] *Ibid.*, s. 22.1.
[51] *Ibid.*, Schedules 2 and 3.
[52] B.C. Order 02-05, March 05, 2002; Quicklaw Cite [2002] B.C.I.P.C.D. No. 10.
[53] Nova Scotia Report FI-01-76, IWK Grace Health Centre, November 13, 2001.
[54] *An Act Respecting the Protection of Personal Information in the Private Sector*, R.S.Q. 1993, c. P-39.1, as am. S.Q. 2001, c. 73 (Bill 75), assented to December 20, 2001.

Electronic Documents Act (PIPEDA).[55] Ontario has recently released a draft for discussion that includes private sector legislation.[56] Other provinces such as British Columbia are considering private sector legislation.

Three provinces have now enacted health information legislation. Manitoba was the first province to proclaim health information legislation in 1997 with the *Personal Health Information Act*.[57] The only other province with health information legislation in force is Alberta with the *Health Information Act*[58] that was proclaimed in April of 2001.

Saskatchewan has enacted but not yet proclaimed health information legislation, with the *Health Information Protection Act*.[59] The Ontario draft for consultation is a combination of health sector and private sector legislation, which creates rights to access and correction of health information.[60]

The Manitoba legislation creates a clear right of access by individuals to their own health information as follows:

> 5(1) Subject to this Act, an individual has a right, on request, to examine and receive a copy of his or her personal health information maintained by a trustee.[61]

Exceptions to access in the Manitoba legislation include disclosure of information that would reasonably be expected to endanger the applicant or another person, personal information about another person, information that would identify a third party who provided information in confidence, practice review and professional disciplinary and risk management information.[62] A recent order in Alberta[63] denied access to practice review information that was compiled pursuant to a patient complaint about a surgeon.

Health information legislation also typically creates a right to request correction and amendment of health information. For example the *Health Information Protection Act* in Saskatchewan says that an individual may request amendment of an error or omission.[64] A notation must be made in the record when an amendment is requested but not made. The trustee must give notice of an amendment or notation to any person that

---

[55] S.C. 2000, c. 5.
[56] *Ontario Draft Privacy of Personal Information Act, 2002*, released February 2002 as a consultation on the draft.
[57] S.M. 1997, c. 51 (C.C.S.M. c. P33.5) proclaimed in force on December 11, 1997.
[58] R.S.A. 2000, c. H-5.
[59] S.S. 1999, c. H-0.021, Royal Assent in May 1999, not yet proclaimed.
[60] *Supra*, n. 56, ss. 56-62.
[61] *Personal Health Information Act*, *supra*, n. 57, s. 5(1).
[62] *Ibid.*, s. 11.
[63] AB Order H2002-002, Calgary Health Region, May 2, 2002.
[64] *Supra*, n. 59, s. 40.

health information has been disclosed to for the previous year, unless the amendment does not impact health services.[65]

ACCESS REQUESTS

There is a growing trend in the number of enactments that authorize access by individuals to their health information. Health agencies and providers should anticipate increasing numbers of requests from hospital patients, nursing home residents, and home care clients for their health records. The practical issue is how to handle requests for access. Policies and procedures should specify in detail how to handle access requests, including the format for making requests.

Guidelines for handling access requests should not only include access requests, but exceptions to access. Other related rights such as the right to correction and amendment should be clearly outlined. Persons with authority to exercise rights of incompetent individuals should be described. Details such as the 30-day time frame and extensions for processing requests, as well as calculation of fees and fee waivers should be addressed. Most legislation requires that individuals be advised of their right to make a complaint to the Commissioner or Ombudsman.

The cost and time required to deal with individuals and to duplicate copies must be addressed by health facilities such as hospitals, nursing homes and community care agencies. Problems arising from poorly managed access requests should be anticipated by Canadian health care agencies and handled through appropriate risk and quality management initiatives.

PRACTICAL CONSIDERATIONS

An adversarial process to gain access to health information is difficult, time-consuming and expensive for everyone involved. A practical and comprehensive approach is in order to assist staff to respond effectively to access requests.

The following considerations should be addressed when developing policies, procedures and guidelines for handling access requests:

- *Form of Request* — Clarify whether requests for access and for correction and amendment must be in writing and in a particu-

---

[65] *Ibid.*

lar form or whether verbal or other means of making requests will be accepted;

- *Health Record* — Describe the documents that constitute the health record such as discharge Summaries, Nurses notes, student notes, x-ray and lab reports, such as temporary records like Kardex and TPR sheets, and electronic records or reports;
- *Substitute Decision-Makers* — Describe who has authority to request access on behalf of other individuals, such as minors, incompetent minors, parents of young children, legal guardians, powers of attorney, agents in personal directives, personal representatives of deceased, written authorizations and statutory lists;
- *Access Process* — Describe the process for providing access to health information such as obtaining copies and viewing the original health record, whether viewing is done alone or with a staff member in the room to ensure integrity of the information;
- *Correction and Amendment Process* — Describe the process for responding to requests for correction and amendment, the process for correction, a statement of disagreement, and notifications;
- *Fees* — Describe when fees will be charged, how to calculate fees, what will happen if individuals cannot afford to pay the fee and when fee waivers will be given;
- *Time* — Establish mechanisms to manage the 30-day time frame and extensions of time for processing access requests;
- *Interpretation* — Indicate whether there will be assistance for interpreting the record such as abbreviations, clinical impressions and laboratory findings;
- *Reviews* — Describe the process for communication to individuals of the right to request a review of decisions of facilities by a Commissioner or Ombudsman; and
- *Staff Education* — Educate and support staff handling access requests.

By addressing these issues, health agencies and providers are more likely to effectively meet the challenges of handling access requests.

8

Confidentiality, Privacy and Disclosure to Third Parties

ISSUES

The twentieth century has seen a vast expansion of health providers and services. Rather than being provided by one physician, the care of an individual now involves dozens and sometimes hundreds of health providers. An episode of care may involve a veritable army of nurses, consulting physicians, technologists and technicians, allied health and administrative personnel. Psychologists, social workers and pastoral care workers have joined the ever-growing team.

The client has gone from being treated by one individual with whom personal information was shared in the home, to being treated by numerous unfamiliar providers in a health facility. That aspect too, has changed. No longer is the individual treated in one agency. An individual may be admitted to a hospital but over the course of the illness may be transferred to a second or third hospital, an outpatient clinic, various laboratory and diagnostic imaging facilities, an extended care facility and then possibly to home care.

Health information flows from the individual to hundreds of other people to provide the sophisticated treatment, which Canadians now expect. Failure to disclose information could result in breach of the standard of care, injury and allegations of negligence. The transfer of information from the individual to those providing treatment is even more important than in the past. With so many people involved in providing treatment, coordination is essential. Coordination can only come about by communication, so that everyone is working with the same information, goals and instructions. Breakdowns in communication may cause harm to the individual. Privacy of the individual, which is achieved through the limited circulation of information, may be threatened.

Privacy was further impinged by the development of government hospital insurance, Medicare and other health care insurance programs in Canada in the 1950s and 1960s. Once the government had the mandate to pay for insured hospital and medical care, it was essential for the government to have information about the providers and services being purchased.

An elaborate system has been established to gather information for purposes of payment. The treatment provided by a physician or the care provided in a hospital must be reported to government health insurance authorities. The name of the individual, the diagnosis and the details of treatment are collected. This enables the government to make payments and to ensure that payments are being made appropriately.

The collection of health information is vital to enable government to administer the health system, and to address overutilization of services and fraudulent billing by health care providers. To determine whether abuse or fraud is taking place, health insurance programs compile facility, physician and client profiles. Individual profiles are compared to the average use or provision of services. The failure of government to audit and manage expenditures would result in severe public criticism. The price, however, is the loss of privacy.

Since public health insurance plans were established, Canadians have increasingly expected provincial and federal governments not only to pay for health services but also to provide services or ensure that insured services are available. It is essential that governments have adequate information about utilization of health services to plan for future requirements. These uses and disclosures of health information move society further away from individual privacy.

CONFIDENTIALITY, PRIVACY AND DISCLOSURE TO THIRD PARTIES

The right to the confidentiality and privacy of health information is not unlimited. Once a health system rather than an individual physician treats the individual, the armies of workers who make up the system require the information or parts of it in order to provide the health services. Failure to have the information communicated from one person to another within the system can cause errors, conflicts in treatment and care, and a general lowering of the standard of care. At times there is a duty to communicate health information beyond those who are actually treating the individual, such as the duty to communicate information for the purposes of obtaining a consultation.

This sharing of information among all those within a facility or a service is not usually recognized by legislation, which establishes a prohibition for breach of confidentiality. It seems to be assumed that the health information of everyone who receives care will be available to all staff with an interest in the care and treatment. The problem is that of restrictions. Can everyone within the facility have access to the health information whether or not they are directly involved in providing care and treatment? What about inter-hospital and inter-agency transfers? Can the transferring facility send confidential information to the receiving facility without express consent of the individual?

The problem is compounded in community-based health services. Home care clients may receive services from a multitude of agencies, including Meals-on-Wheels, transportation agencies, nursing agencies, physiotherapists, respiratory services and homemakers. Representatives from one agency may observe needs or problems not apparent to another agency. A concern arises regarding the propriety of one agency contacting the other. Without permission from the client, the sharing of information could be perceived as a breach of confidentiality. The problem can be exacerbated if a referral agency discourages inter-agency contact. The net effect could be substandard client care as the cost of maintaining "confidentiality".

Staff may use health information for purposes of teaching and research. It is an open question whether this use is a breach of confidentiality and privacy or whether the client has given implied consent by entering a facility that does teaching and research. One can extend this argument to use for purposes of audit, internal monitoring and peer review.

Because of the uncertainty of the law on this matter, it is incumbent on facilities to establish strict guidelines as to who may or may not see health information. There may be practical problems where staff members have a legitimate interest in seeing part but not all of the health information. Discretion must be used in these matters.

Health agency guidelines should address the release of information to third parties. It is at that point that client permission or legal authority should be sought. The release, for example, of hospital information to a social service agency or a school, or to an insurance company or to the police, is not a practice that most individuals would ordinarily expect. Therefore, consent cannot be implied and should be express and documented.

Guidelines should be in place governing conduct that could breach confidentiality and privacy. Casual conversations in which confidential client information is overheard in an open clinic or leaving charts in a public area are common instances where confidentiality can be breached. Breaches can easily occur in the telephone-dependent home care industry. A receptionist may be quite comfortable divulging client information to someone who represents himself or herself as the representative of a familiar-sounding community resource. However, the caller may be making misrepresentations to gather personal information about a client.

Consider the following illustration. A home care client is rushed to hospital. A break-and-enter ring working in the neighborhood notices no activity at the home. Lights do not go on and off at the usual time. They know from observing the area that the resident receives home care services. To make certain that no one is at home, they call the agency and indicate that they have home care supplies to deliver but no one answers the door. They ask the receptionist, "Is something wrong?" The receptionist says the client is in hospital and is not expected to return home for two weeks. By divulging health information, the receptionist has not only breached confidentiality, but has also set the stage for a "safe" break-and-enter.

Orientation and in-service education sessions are a must in terms of training staff about the do's and don'ts of confidentiality and privacy. The training should not simply be directed at health care professionals. Receptionists, secretaries, information technology, housekeeping and casual support personnel should receive education about the improprieties and dangers of unauthorized disclosure of health information to third parties. Expectations of confidentiality should be clearly described to external service providers such agencies performing microfilming, shredding, and storage functions, in contracts and policies and procedures.

ETHICS AND PROFESSIONAL PRACTICE

Health information obtained by a physician in the care and treatment of an individual is confidential and is a secret not to be inappropriately divulged. Other health professions, disciplines and agencies share this duty of confidentiality. This duty of confidentiality has been expressed in codes of ethics of health professionals since the Hippocratic Oath, which says:

> Whatsoever things I see or hear concerning the life of man, in any attendance on the sick or even apart therefrom, which ought not to be noised abroad, I will keep secret thereon, counting such things to be as sacred secrets.[1]

Privacy has been described as the right to be let alone or the right of individuals to control the disclosure of information about them. An example of a recent code of ethics is the Canadian Medical Association Code, which says:

---

[1]   C. DeWitt, *Privileged Communications Between Physician and Patient* (Springfield, Ill.: C.C. Thomas, 1958) at 23; a slightly different version is reproduced in J.K. Mason and R.A. McCall Smith, *Law and Medical Ethics*, 4th ed. (London: Butterworths, 1994), Appendix A.

The right of privacy is fundamental in a free and democratic society. It includes a patient's right to determine with whom he or she will share information and to know of and exercise control over use, disclosure and access concerning any information collected about him or her. The right of privacy and consent are essential to the trust and integrity of the patient-physician relationship...[2]

Mr. Justice Horace Krever in the *Royal Commission of Inquiry into the Confidentiality of Health Records in Ontario* made two important assertions. The first is that society values confidentiality of health information, which is not to be freely disclosed.[3] The second is that everyone should have access to their own health information.[4]

The Canadian Health Record Association has developed the following Code of Practice for Safeguarding Health Information:[5]

1. All individuals, institutions and organizations maintaining, handling or processing health information shall
   - have written policies regulating access to, release of transmittal and destruction of health information;
   - educate all their employees with regard to maintaining confidentiality of information, and have them sign a pledge of confidentiality. This procedure shall apply also to researchers, volunteers, contracted individuals and employees of firms and corporations performing contract work.
2. Health information shall be accessed or released only for:
   - *direct care use* — when requested by a physician or health care facility responsible for the direct care of the individual;
   - *individual use* — when authorized by the individual or his legally authorized representative;
   - *secondary use* — when requested by properly authorized persons or agencies;
   - *legal use* — when required by law.
3. Requests for confidential information should be in writing; however, policies governing verbal requests shall be as outlined by the individual agency.
4. Any authorization for release of information shall be an original and specific as to: source, content, recipient, purpose and time limitations. Reproductions of original signatures shall not be accepted.

---

[2] Canadian Medical Association, *CMA Health Information Privacy Code*, approved August 15, 1998, at 8.

[3] H. Krever, *Royal Commission of Inquiry into the Confidentiality of Health Records in Ontario*, 1980, vol. 1, at 7 [hereinafter referred to as the "Krever Report"].

[4] *Ibid.*, at 9.

[5] Canadian Health Record Association, *Code of Practice for Safeguarding Health Information*, 1987.

5. Information released to authorized persons shall not be made available to any other party without further authorization.
6. Health information and records shall be kept in a secured area and not left unattended in areas accessible to unauthorized individuals.
7. In research, individual confidentiality shall be maintained in the handling of information and any reporting or publication of findings.
8. When health information is sent to any service organization for processing, the contract shall include an undertaking by the recipient that confidentiality will be maintained.
9. The authorized destruction of health information shall be by effective shredding, burning or erasure.
10. Any misuse of health information shall be reported to the responsible authority.

The Canadian Council on Health Services Accreditation (CCHSA), formerly known as the Canadian Council on Health Facilities Accreditation, requires accredited organizations to protect the confidentiality, security, and integrity of data and information.[6] Included in the steps it must take are, defining and applying levels of security and integrity to data and information; restricting, controlling and monitoring access; safeguarding data and information against loss, accident and destruction, and corruption; adhering to formal policies and procedures; and conducting regular internal checks.[7] The Council also requires that there is evidence that the organization has been successful in this.[8]

A health professional may be disciplined by a professional regulatory body for divulging health information without justification,[9] as this disclosure is in contravention of ethical and professional standards. Professional regulatory bodies are responsible to protect the public and to ensure that members meet professional standards of practice. A breach of confidentiality or privacy constitutes professional misconduct and may form the basis of disciplinary proceedings including the loss of licensure. For example, when the College of Pharmacists in British Columbia found a number of pharmacists guilty of professional misconduct for inappropriately accessing PharmaNet patient records, the pharmacists received licence suspensions and fines.[10]

---

[6] Ottawa, CCHSA, Information Management, s. 7.0.
[7] *Ibid.*, s. 7.1.
[8] *Ibid.*, s. 7.4.
[9] See *e.g.*, *Code of Ethics Regulation*, Alta. Reg. 456/83, s. 2(3), enacted under the *Nursing Profession Act* in Alberta.
[10] College of Pharmacists of British Columbia, Bulletin, May/June 1999, Vol. 24, No. 3, at 3, March/April 2000, Vol. 24, No. 3, at 3 and 5.

COMMON LAW

Health agencies and professionals can be sued for breach of confidentiality or privacy. Legal action for the inappropriate disclosure of health information could involve a number of possibilities. One possibility is breach of contract. It would be rare to have a written contract dealing with confidentiality or privacy signed by a patient and provider, so a court might imply a contractual obligation of confidentiality. In *Mammone v. Bakan*,[11] a doctor was ordered to send a plaintiff's post-accident file to defendant's counsel, but instead the doctor sent the entire medical record. The plaintiff successfully sued the doctor for damages in breach of contract.

Another possibility is an action for breach of confidentiality. This cause of action is uncertain in Canadian common law. The Supreme Court of Canada has recognized a duty of confidentiality based on equitable principles.[12] This principle was subsequently accepted by the Ontario High Court of Justice in a doctor-patient breach of confidentiality case.[13] The Supreme Court of Canada recently emphasized the duty of confidentiality arising from the fiduciary relationship between physician and patient in *McInerney v. MacDonald*.[14]

Another possibility is an action for invasion of privacy. Although a tort for breach of privacy developed in the United States, this did not happen in Canada. The five provinces of British Columbia,[15] Saskatchewan,[16] Manitoba,[17] Quebec[18] and Newfoundland and Labrador[19] have enacted "privacy" acts, which enable civil action to be taken for violations of privacy. A plaintiff was successful under the B.C. legislation in *Hollinsworth v. BCTV* when a video of the plaintiff's hair treatment was released to the media and played on the air without consent.[20] Despite this legislation, there have been few successful cases litigated.[21]

It has also been suggested that a patient may take legal action against a physician or other health worker or institution on the basis of negli-

---

[11] [1989] B.C.J. No. 2438 (QL) (S.C.).
[12] *Slavutych v. Baker*, [1976] 1 S.C.R. 254, [1975] 4 W.W.R. 620, 55 D.L.R. (3d) 224, 38 C.R.N.S. 306, 75 C.L.L.C. 14.
[13] *Damien v. O'Mulvenny* (1981), 34 O.R. (2d) 448, 128 D.L.R. (3d) 258, 19 C.C.L.T. 48, at 50 (H.C.J.).
[14] [1992] 2 S.C.R. 138, on appeal from the Court of Appeal of New Brunswick.
[15] *Privacy Act*, R.S.B.C. 1979, c. 336.
[16] *Privacy Act*, R.S.S. 1978, c. P-24.
[17] *Privacy Act*, R.S.M. 1970, c. 74.
[18] *Charter of Human Rights and Freedoms*, R.S.Q. 1977, c. C-12, ss. 5 and 9; art. 1053 C.C.Q.
[19] *Privacy Act*, R.S.N.L. 1990, c. P-22.
[20] (1996), 34 C.C.L.T. (2d) 95 (B.C.S.C.), affd. (1998), 113 B.C.A.C. 304 (C.A.).
[21] C. McNairn and A. Scott, *Privacy Law in Canada* (Toronto: Butterworths Canada Ltd., 2001) at 73.

gence in breaching confidentiality. Rodgers-Magnet discusses this possibility[22] in light of the Supreme Court of New Zealand case of *Furniss v. Fitchett*.[23] A breach of confidentiality may be a failure to abide by the average, reasonable and prudent standard in the circumstances and may amount to negligence when injuries were suffered.

Prosecutions pursuant to statutory provisions are rare. Disciplinary action through professional regulatory bodies is often difficult to prove and is limited to breaches of confidentiality by members of professional registration bodies. Because of the uncertainty as to whether or not a person has a cause of action for breach of confidentiality or privacy it has been recommended that a statutory right should be created. This right would permit a patient whose health information has been disclosed without authorization to start a legal action. The action could be brought against anyone who has a duty to keep health information confidential and who unjustifiably discloses the information.[24]

Enforcing rights of confidentiality and privacy is difficult. Individuals may not even be aware that health information has been improperly disclosed. In most cases there is no demonstrable injury to the individual. Litigation entails a public court process and further disclosure of confidential information. Protection of confidentiality and privacy is a balance between the right to privacy and the provision of care, which requires the timely flow of information.

Confidentiality is often an issue in litigation where third parties seek access to health information. Sometimes litigators request permission to secure copies of confidential medical information from other individuals when they themselves are embroiled in malpractice actions. In a British Columbia case,[25] the plaintiff made such a request on the basis that

> it was necessary to know what other professional obligations the doctors at the hospital had to meet during the time that this patient was being attended in order to determine whether or not the other obligations of the doctors and the nurses had detracted from the proper care which ought to have been administered to the plaintiff.[26]

A judge in chambers agreed with this request with the proviso that the names of other individuals be removed. In affirming the decision the British Columbia Court of Appeal noted that the plaintiff does have the

---

[22] S. Rodgers-Magnet, *Common Law Remedies for Disclosure of Confidential Medical Information.*

[23] [1958] N.Z.L.R. 396.

[24] *Krever Report*, Vol. I (1980), *supra*, n. 3, at 15.

[25] *Anderson v. University of British Columbia* (February 7, 1991), Doc. No. CA 013449, (B.C.C.A.).

[26] *Ibid.*, at 2.

right to see documents, which may lead to a line of inquiry that may "directly or indirectly assist him in his cause".[27]

Other judicial decisions reinforce this principle,[28] even in cases in which the information at issue is of a sensitive nature.[29] The issue of confidentiality and third party access takes on considerable importance with AIDS. Even in this sensitive area, however, the courts do not seem reluctant to permit the plaintiff access to health information.

Such was the circumstance in an Ontario case in which the estate of a deceased person sued a hospital for supplying the individual with blood and blood products contaminated with the AIDS virus.[30] The plaintiff argued that the defendant breached its warranty of fitness regarding the blood as implied under common law and in provincial legislation governing the sale of goods.

The hospital, in turn, commenced a third party action against the supplier of the blood, the Canadian Red Cross Society. The hospital wanted contribution and indemnification from the Society for the breach of warranty claim made by the plaintiff. In the alternative, the hospital argued that the Red Cross had been negligent in manufacturing and supplying the blood and blood products.

During the course of the pre-trial component of the case, a Master of the Ontario Court of Justice ordered the Red Cross to allow the plaintiff to examine the blood donor records for individuals who supplied blood for the deceased patient. The Master imposed some restrictions. The Red Cross challenged the Master's order, asserting that its blood donor system was based on individuals providing blood in a confidential manner. Without the prospect of anonymity, the Red Cross claimed, it would be impossible to operate a volunteer blood supply program.

The Court rejected the Red Cross Society's argument. It noted that the confidentiality requirement was a self-imposed phenomenon found in its policies and procedures. Furthermore, there never was a confidential relationship between donors and the Red Cross. The Court also pointed out that without the requested information, the plaintiff would be unlikely to establish the necessary elements of the lawsuit. Weighing the

---

[27] *Ibid.*, at 6.

[28] See *e.g.*, *Airton v. Hespe* (July 10, 1989), Doc. No. 8801271 (B.C.S.C.).

[29] See *R. v. Lines*, (1986), 27 C.C.C. (3d) 377 (N.W.T. C.A.), affg. [1986] N.W.T.R. 21, 22 C.C.C. (3d) 230 (S.C.), involving disclosure of notes made by a public health nurse in a child abduction case. See also, *Crawford v. G.D. Searle & Co. of Canada Ltd.* (1987), 12 B.C.L.R. (2d) 192 (S.C.) in which defence counsel sought to control the way in which the plaintiff could disseminate information out of concern that it could defeat U.S. rulings which had prohibited production of information from the defendant's American subsidiaries.

[30] *Sharpe Estate v. Northwestern General Hospital* (1991), 2 O.R. (3d) 40 (Gen. Div.).

competing interests in the case, the Court found that the search should be permitted to proceed.[31]

The *Sharpe* case and other litigation involving third party access demonstrates that confidentiality of health information is not an absolute certainty. The mere fact that a health agency states in its policies and procedures that records are "confidential" does not preclude a court finding to the contrary. The rulings suggest that health agencies should take a fresh look at their health information policies and procedures. If individuals, nursing home residents, home care clients, or human research trial subjects are assured that their health information is confidential, a trap may be in place waiting to be sprung. An agency may not be able to abide by such assurances, particularly in light of court directives to disclose the information.

The fine points of third party access to health information require cogent legal advice. Legal counsel should scrutinize relevant legislation and regulations as well as case law on the topic. Once the requirements and limitations on confidentiality are known, the agency can begin to build its policies and procedures. This includes training staff in the hospital admissions office or a counselor in an alcohol detoxification centre not to make false promises about information being maintained "confidentially". Clients should be told of common disclosures.

Disclosure of health information during the litigation process was recently addressed in a court decision[32] that considered the *Health Information Act* in Alberta. Legal counsel for the defendant applied to interview the physician who treated the plaintiff's mother and who had been subpoenaed to give evidence for the plaintiff at trial. Justice Marshall permitted this interview in accordance with requirements of the litigation process.

The commencement of legal action against a health care professional has been regarded as a waiver of the usual obligation of confidentiality that arises in the fiduciary relationship. However, the continuation of the fiduciary duty of a health care professional still continues on to some extent even after a patient brings litigation against that person. This obligation flows from the patient having something akin to a proprietary interest in the information.

In a recent decision in Alberta, Justice Burrows held that the duty of confidentiality continues notwithstanding the litigation.[33] The Court held that a treating doctor should not participate in an interview with defence counsel without involving the plaintiff. Confidentiality in litigation is waived only to the extent necessary to accommodate the defendant's

---

[31]   *Ibid.*
[32]   *Pozdzik (Next friend of) v. Wilson* (January 11, 2002), Doc. No. 9303 01105 (Alta. Q.B.).
[33]   *Stoodley v. Ferguson* (March 16, 2001), Doc. No. 9603 23579 (Alta. Q.B.).

right to relevant information in the action. This prevents a physician from releasing information to anyone other than the defendant in the presence of the plaintiff, releasing information not relevant to the action and requires the plaintiff to be kept fully informed of information disclosed by the physician.

DUTY TO WARN

Health professionals, particularly physicians, may have a duty to breach confidentiality to warn a third party of danger as a result of an individual's health condition. The leading American case is the California case of *Tarasoff v. The Regents of the University of California et al.*[34] In that case a student informed his psychologist that he intended to kill a particular student. He subsequently carried out his threat. The family of the deceased sued and claimed they should have been warned. The Supreme Court of California agreed with that position.

There are some judicial decisions in Canada that suggest that some individuals may be duty bound to divulge confidential information for the benefit of others. In *Hendrick v. De Marsh*[35] a man who just completed a prison sentence for break and enter was accepted as a boarder in a boarding house. The parole officer responsible for De Marsh sought out the accommodations. He did not tell the boarding house owners that the man had a propensity for setting fires, a manifestation of his underlying personality disorder. Subsequently, De Marsh set fire to the boarding home.

Although the action was held to be statute-barred under the Ontario *Authorities Protection Act*,[36] the Court said a special relationship existed between the parole officer and the owners of the boarding house in that carelessness on their part could likely cause harm to the plaintiffs. The parole officer had represented the would-be tenant to be honest and reliable while knowing that he had an underlying disorder that could pose a risk of harm. The judge indicated that were it not for the statute, he would have found against the parole officer and the Ministry of Correctional Services.[37]

In *Smith v. Jones*,[38] the Supreme Court of Canada considered whether the public safety exception applied to the disclosure of health informa-

---

[34] 551 P.2d 334 (Cal. 1976).
[35] (1984), 40 O.R. (2d) 463, 28 C.C.L.T. 207, 6 D.L.R. (4th) 713 (H.C.J.), affd. (1986), 54 O.R. (2d) 185, 26 D.L.R. (4th) 130 (C.A.).
[36] R.S.O. 1970, c. 374, s. 11.
[37] *Ibid.*
[38] (1999), 169 D.L.R. (4th) 385 (S.C.C.).

tion. In the *Smith* case a psychiatrist assessed an accused at the request of legal counsel for the accused. The accused was charged with aggravated sexual assault of a prostitute. The psychiatrist determined that the accused had a number of serious psychological disorders and posed a continuing danger to the public. The psychiatrist sought a court order to disclose his psychiatrist's report and warn the public.

The Supreme Court of Canada said the facts in this case justified disclosure, even where this meant the loss of solicitor-client privilege. The Court said that three factors must be present to meet the criteria for disclosure. The factors were: a clear risk to an identifiable group of persons, a serious risk of bodily harm including serious psychological harm or death and an imminent danger.[39]

The *Hendrick* case says that a "special relationship" gives rise to a duty to warn of impending risk. The question is what constitutes a "special relationship" in the health care context? Is it the relationship between caregivers and recipients of health services? What about a home care client who is being abused by a son? The *Smith* case creates a common law exception that allows disclosure when the criteria for imminent danger exist.

There are few cut-and-dried answers. A clearer answer now exists in some legislative enactments. However, even where legislation exists the facts still need to be applied to the legislative criteria. Other health agencies and professionals are still waiting for a legislative answer. Professionals are left to balance codes of ethics against concerns about legal consequences for divulging confidential information. Individual decision-making will lead to inconsistencies. The most practical solution is for health agencies and professional groups to set clear-cut guidelines regarding the duty to warn. Once communicated, there may be less reticence to report known or suspected situations, which pose a serious risk of harm to individuals or the public.

CONSENT TO DISCLOSURE

The general rule is that health information can be disclosed either pursuant to consent or as authorized by law. Consent may take various forms including implied and express consent, oral and written consent and opt-in and opt-out consent. The ability to consent rests with the individual when the individual is a competent adult and sometimes when the individual is a competent minor.

---

[39] *Ibid.*, at 408-411.

Depending upon the provincial legislation, the authority to consent may also rest with substitute decision-makers such as the guardian of an incompetent minor, a personal representative of the deceased, a legal guardian or trustee, an agent in a personal directive or living will, the nearest relative under mental health legislation, a power of attorney appointed by an attorney or a person with written authorization of the individual.[40]

Disclosure of health information to entities such as the press and the police is a controversial issue that arises in various circumstances, such as with prominent figures and victims of violent crime. The press may attempt to take photographs or question health personnel. The police may demand access to the individual or to their health information. Policies should set out details such as who will field questions from the media and the police. Even whether or not confirmation can be given about whether an individual is in the care of the agency and geographic location should be addressed.

Sometimes the media and the police can be of great assistance to health agencies such as when individuals go unexpectedly missing from hospitals or residents elope from longterm care facilities. Public service announcements may be broadcast on radio and television or printed in newspapers. Invoking a media campaign and police services may help to locate missing individuals. From a legal perspective, reporting a missing person to the press may amount to unauthorized disclosure of confidential information, particularly when details about the nature of the individual's illness, medication requirements, identifying scars and other related matters are revealed.

Authorization to release details is important. If the person who is missing is incompetent, permission to disclose to the media might come from a surrogate decision-maker. The issue might be addressed as a component of the consent during admission process, particularly when the individual has cognitive deficiencies or the contingency of an elopement exists. Individuals, residents or their surrogate decision-makers could be advised that agency policy permits disclosure of some information when deemed necessary to prevent harm.

Consent may need to meet specific legislative criteria, such as in the *Health Information Act* in Alberta.[41] Provincial legislation may require consent before disclosure by electronic means, for disclosure to researchers for research purposes, before researchers can contact individuals for further information for research, and when information is collected by

---

[40] *Health Information Act*, R.S.A. 2000, c. H-5, s. 104; *Personal Health Information Act*, S.M. 1997, c. 51 (C.C.S.M. c. P33.5), s. 60; *Health Information Protection Act*, S.S. 1999, c. H-0.021, s. 56, *Ontario Draft Privacy of Personal Information Act*, 2002, Part II.

[41] *Ibid.*, ss. 34, 59.

hidden devices such as a video cameras.[42] Provincial legislation may provide for obtaining signatures to consent with electronic signatures.[43]

These issues should be addressed in agency policy. The details of any policy must be carefully developed with legal counsel to make certain the disclosure exception is consistent with provincial law. Consent is discussed in more detail in Chapter 13 — Documenting Consent.

LEGISLATIVE REQUIREMENTS FOR CONFIDENTIALITY AND PRIVACY

In addition to ethical and professional requirements, health information may also be protected by health sector statutes. These statutes may deal with third party payers such as the provincial health insurance program, various health facilities such as hospitals and nursing homes, certain diseases such as cancer and mental health, and certain types of care such as home care, public health and ambulance services.

For example, the *Hospitals Act* in Newfoundland and Labrador states that no hospital authority shall allow any person access to, or disclose to any person any information contained in, the records of the hospital authority.[44] Various exceptions to the duty of confidentiality exist in the statute.

The *Hospitals Act* of Nova Scotia[45] makes it clear that confidentiality applies not only to current patients but to past patients as well. The legislation states that the particulars of a hospital concerning an individual in the hospital or an individual formerly in the hospital shall be confidential and shall not be available to any person or agency except with the consent or authorization of the individual concerned.[46] Various exceptions are included.

Hospitals are not the only type of health facility with enactments requiring health information to be kept in a confidential manner. Nursing homes have the general principle of confidentiality established by legislation. The general statutory rule of confidentiality and privacy is also modified by exceptions, which describe specific instances where health information can be disclosed. Typical of this approach is the New Brunswick *Nursing Homes Act*[47] and the regulations promulgated under

---

[42] *Ibid.*, ss. 23, 50(1)(a), 55, 59.
[43] *Ibid.*, ss. 34(4) and 59(4).
[44] R.S.N.L. 1990, c. H-9, s. 35(2).
[45] S.N.S. 1989, c. 208.
[46] *Ibid.*, s. 71.
[47] S.N.B. 1982, c. N-11, as amended, s. 14(2).

the Alberta *Nursing Homes Act*.[48] The Ontario *Independent Health Facilities Act* also addresses the scope of confidentiality and third party access.[49]

An interesting legislative mechanism granting third party access to health information involves physicians as clients. Under the Newfoundland and Labrador *Medical Act*[50] when a doctor is admitted for treatment of mental illness or addiction to drugs or alcohol, the chief executive officer of the hospital and the attending physician of a doctor must file a written report with the Registrar of the College of Physicians and Surgeons. At the time of discharge, the attending physician must provide a medical report to the Registrar indicating whether or not the doctor is fit to resume the practice of medicine.[51]

Legislative requirements for the protection of confidentiality and privacy of personal information that include health information in the public sector exist in the access to information and protection of privacy legislation in the provinces,[52] territories,[53] and at the federal level.[54] Similar legislation covers some personal information in the private sector in Canada.[55] The provinces with health information legislation have specific provisions that establish the duty of confidentiality and privacy for

---

[48] *Operation of Nursing Homes Regulation*, Alta. Reg. 232/85, s. 12.

[49] R.S.O. 1990, c. I.3, ss. 36-37.

[50] R.S.N.L. 1990, c. M-4.

[51] *Ibid.*

[52] *Freedom of Information and Protection of Privacy Act*, R.S.B.C. 1996, c. 165; *Protection of Personal Information Act*, S.N.B. 2001, c. P-19.1, proclaimed April 2001; *Freedom of Information Act*, R.S.N.L. 1990, c. F-25, Royal Assent but not yet proclaimed; *Privacy Act*, R.S.N.L. 1990, c. P-22, Royal Assent but not yet proclaimed; *Freedom of Information and Protection of Privacy Act*, S.N.S. 1993, c. 5; *Freedom of Information and Protection of Privacy Act*, R.S.O. 1990, c. F.31; *Municipal Freedom of Information and Protection of Privacy Act*, R.S.O. 1990, c. M.-56; *Freedom of Information and Protection of Privacy Act (No. 2)*, S.P.E.I. 2001, c. 37 (Bill 47), Royal Assent on May 15, 2001, not yet proclaimed; *Act Respecting Access to Documents held by Public Bodies and the Protection of Personal Information*, R.S.Q. 1993, c. A-2.1, enacted June 22, 1982; *Freedom of Information and Protection of Privacy Act*, S.S. 1990-91, c. F-22.01; *Local Authority Freedom of Information and Protection of Privacy Act*, S.S. 1990-91, c. L-27.1; also refer to An Inside Look at the Office of the Information and Privacy Commissioner, Health Law Seminars, LESA, April 2002, at 6-7.

[53] *Access to Information and Protection of Privacy Act (Nunavut)*, S.N.W.T. 1994, c. 20 (Nunavut, enacted under s. 76.05 of *Nunavut Act*); *Access to Information and Protection of Privacy Act*, S.N.W.T. 1994, c. 20; *Access to Information and Protection of Privacy Act*, S.Y. 1995, c. 1.

[54] *Access to Information Act*, R.S.C. 1985, c. A-1; *Privacy Act*, R.S.C. 1985, c. P-21.

[55] *An Act Respecting the Protection of Personal Information in the Private Sector*, R.S.Q. 1993, c. P-39.1, as am. S.Q. 2001, c. 73 (Bill 75), assented to December 20, 2001; *Personal Information Protection and Electronic Documents Act*, S.C. 2000, c. 5; *Ontario Draft Privacy of Personal Information Act, 2002*, released February 2002; as a consultation on the draft, British Columbia is conducting a consultation for legislation in the private sector.

health information.[56] These statutes also contain exceptions to the protection of confidentiality and privacy.

LEGISLATIVE AUTHORITY FOR DISCLOSURE TO THIRD PARTIES

There are numerous legislative exceptions to the confidentiality and privacy of health information. These exceptions authorize disclosure without consent pursuant to statutory exceptions to confidentiality that cover a wide range of purposes from providing care to disclosing information to a Minister. The exceptions may be discretionary or compulsory or may arise when requested by an official. Numerous exceptions arise under legislation that is not health sector legislation such as under vital statistics legislation.

The most specific disclosure provisions arise within health information legislation.[57] It should be noted that there are various types of health information defined in legislation that is governed by slightly different disclosure rules. For example, there is diagnostic, treatment and care information, registration information including the personal health number (PHN) and health services provider information.

Health information legislation contains general rules for disclosing health information. For example, in Alberta, health information must be disclosed as aggregate information with the highest level of anonymity whenever possible.[58] The limiting rule applies, which means that only the minimum amount of health information may be collected, used and disclosed.[59] Any express wishes of the individual and any relevant factors must be considered.[60]

Health information may only be disclosed when the person disclosing has made a reasonable effort to ensure the authenticity of the recipient so the information is being disclosed to an authorized individual.[61] The person disclosing must also make a reasonable effort to ensure the health

---

[56] *Personal Health Information Act*, S.M. 1997, c. 51 (C.C.S.M. c. P33.5), proclaimed in force on December 11, 1997; *Health Information Act*, R.S.A. 2000, c. H-5; *Health Information Protection Act*, S.S. 1999, c. H-0.021, Royal Assent in May 1999, not yet proclaimed; *Ontario Draft Privacy of Personal Information Act*, 2002.

[57] *Personal Health Information Act, supra*, n. 56, ss. 22, 23, 24(3)(c); *Health Information Act, supra*, n. 56, ss. 35-40, 46-47, 50, 70; *Health Information Protection Act, supra*, n. 56, ss. 18, 20, 27-30; *Ontario Draft Privacy of Personal Information Act, 2002*, ss. 37-48.

[58] See *e.g., Health Information Act, supra*, n. 56, s. 57.

[59] *Ibid.*, s. 58(1).

[60] *Ibid.*, s. 58(2).

[61] *Ibid.*, s. 45.

information is accurate and complete.[62] The custodian must advise the recipient in writing of the purpose for the disclosure and the authority for the disclosure.[63] Notations including the name of the recipient, date and purpose of the disclosure and a description of the information disclosed must be prepared and the notations must be kept for 10 years after the disclosure.[64]

Health information legislation requires administrative, technical and physical safeguards. For example, in Alberta, privacy impact assessments must be prepared for all changes or new health information systems that impact privacy.[65] Special attention must be paid to the adequate disposal of health information. Adequate security measures must be in place. Contractual agreements with the provisions specified must be in place between custodians and researchers, with information managers and for transborder data flow of health information.[66] Data matching requires that certain precautions be taken such as preparing a privacy impact assessment, notifying the Commissioner, and when research is involved the approval of a designated Research Ethics Board is required.[67]

Disclosures to third parties are not typically caught by the fee schedule, which applies to access requests by the individual.[68] However, custodians may decide to charge the same fees for all disclosures for administrative reasons. Disclosures in contravention of the legislation are an offence and subject to a $50,000 fine that is enforced by prosecution for breach of the legislation.[69] Health information legislation typically provides remedies for individual complaints for refusal of access or breach of privacy and for a custodian wanting to review the decision of another custodian who is refusing to disclose health information.[70] Health information legislation is typically enforced by a commissioner or an ombudsman. A commissioner may have broad order-making and other powers for disclosures in contravention of the legislation.[71]

---

[62] *Ibid.*, s. 61.
[63] *Ibid.*, s. 42.
[64] *Ibid.*, s. 41.
[65] *Ibid.*, s. 64.
[66] *Ibid.*, s. 64; *Health Information Regulation*, Alta. Reg. 70/2001, s. 8(4).
[67] See *Health Information Regulation*, *ibid.*, s. 8(4).
[68] *Ibid.*, ss. 9-13, Schedule.
[69] See *Health Information Act*, *supra*, n. 56, s. 107(6).
[70] *Ibid.*, s. 73.
[71] *Ibid.*, ss. 80, 84-88.

LEGISLATIVE AUTHORITY FOR DISCLOSURES WITHOUT CONSENT

Disclosures of health information that may be authorized without consent include:

- provision of health services
  - other custodians or trustees
  - persons providing continuing treatment and care
  - health services in a penal or other custodial institution
  - descendants of a deceased individual when needed to provide health services to other individuals
- best interests
  - incompetent individual when in his or her best interests
- family and close friends
  - general information about condition, diagnosis and prognosis
  - contacting when individual is injured, ill or deceased
- determining eligibility to receive health services
- research
- education
- internal management
  - planning
  - resource allocation
  - policy development
  - quality improvement
  - practice review and disciplinary proceedings
    - investigations
    - disciplinary proceedings
    - practice review
    - inspections
  - monitoring and evaluation
  - audit, investigations and inspections
  - reporting
  - processing payment for health services
  - human resource management
- health professional bodies
- fraud
  - limit abuse
  - prevent an offence
- legal proceedings
  - court orders including subpoenas, warrants, notices to attend
  - court and quasi-judicial proceedings.
- police

- investigating an offence involving a life-threatening injury to the individual
- imminent danger
  - avert or minimize an imminent danger to health or safety
- successors
  - custodians transferring records to a successor
  - archives for storage
- health system
  - ministers of Department of Health
  - agreements with ministers and governments
  - directed or required disclosures to the minister or other custodians
- enactments
  - public health & safety, mandatory reporting
    - child abuse[72]
    - elder abuse[73]
    - unexpected death[74]
    - unsafe drivers[75]
- compensation regimes
  - workers' compensation[76]
  - occupational health and safety
  - insurance and benefit plans
- statistical
  - vital statistics[77]
  - elections
  - census

INTERNATIONAL TRENDS

The emphasis on health information confidentiality is not exclusively North American. As part of the European Community's (EC) 1992 move to greater unity, new requirements have been put in place governing access to personal information.[78] Anyone doing business with EC member

---

[72] See *e.g., Child and Family Services Act,* R.S.O. 1990, c. C.11, s. 72.

[73] *Adult Protection Act,* S.N.S. 1989, c. 2, s. 5.

[74] *Fatality Inquiries Act,* S.M. 1989-90, c. 30, s. 9(7); see *e.g., Coroners Act,* R.S.Q. 1977, c. C-68; *Coroners Act,* R.S.N.B. 1973, c. C-23.

[75] *Highway Traffic Act,* R.S.O. 1990, c. H.8, s. 93.

[76] *Workers Compensation Act,* R.S.M. 1987, c. W200, s. 18.

[77] See *e.g., Vital Statistics Act,* R.S.N.S. 1989, c. 494, ss. 3, 17.

[78] *Organisation for Economic Cooperation and Development (OECD) Guidelines,* issued in 1980, directive 95/46/EC on the Protection of Individuals processing personal data and on the free movement of the data; Regulation (EC) 45/2001 for processing personal data of

countries must have a system in place to assure privacy of personal information. Such matters as collecting data, assuring that the content of records is timely, accurate, and up-to-date are covered in the requirements. Restrictions on usage, information storage security, and right of correction are also contemplated in the new requirements.[79]

The United Kingdom, a member state of the EC has taken specific steps with regard to health care record information.[80] It is likely that other nations will follow to make certain there is harmony on this issue.

As a nation, which now does considerable trade with the EC, Canada must make certain that there is compliance with these requirements. Canada adopted the OECD Guidelines in 1984 and proceeded to adopt the CSA Model Code in 1996. Steps have been taken to adopt the CSA Code by the International Standards Association (ISO). Individual provinces have all proceeded to enact FOIP legislation that has completely changed the way in which the law views the notion of confidentiality and disclosure of health information. The trend in Canada is towards the adoption of not just public but also private sector legislation.[81]

PRACTICAL CONSIDERATIONS

1. *Duty of confidentiality and privacy* — Ensure that facility policies, procedures and guidelines clearly describe the duties of confidentiality and privacy for health information. Establish a pledge of confidentiality or an oath of confidentiality at the beginning of employment and consider periodic renewal such as on an annual basis.

2. *Establish mechanisms to protect confidentiality and privacy* — Ensure that facility practices include best practices and ongoing review to incorporate new standards, legislation and common law principles. Explicit mechanisms should be in place to ensure that confidentiality and privacy are protected and that exceptions are understood. Mechanisms such as contracts, privacy impact assessments, consent processes and forms and ongoing staff education are important initiatives.

---

community institutions and bodies and free movement of the data; Directive 97/66/EC for personal data and protection of privacy in the telecommunications sector; *Treaty on the European Union and European Convention for Protection of Human Rights and Fundamental Freedoms; EU Charter of Fundamental Rights*, December 7, 2000.

[79] *Ibid.*

[80] See *Access to Health Record Act 1990* (U.K.), 1990, c. 23.

[81] *An Act Respecting the Protection of Personal Information in the Private Sector*, R.S.Q. 1993, c. P-39.1, as am. S.Q. 2001, c. 73 (Bill 75), assented to December 20, 2001; *Personal Information Protection and Electronic Documents Act*, S.C. 2000, c. 5; *Ontario Draft Privacy of Personal Information Act, 2002*, released February 2002 as a consultation on the draft; British Columbia is conducting a consultation for legislation in the private sector.

3. *Disclosure to third parties* — Ensure that exceptions to confidentiality and privacy that are routinely encountered by the facility are described in an explicit fashion. Ensure that a facility resource such as the appropriate contact person is listed, for example for requests from the media and police.

The law surrounding confidentiality, privacy and third party access to health information is far from settled. It is bound to take on new dimensions as society comes to grips with issues such as biometrics, genetic information, bioterrism and the duty to warn. For those involved in safeguarding and disclosing health information, it is imperative to keep up with changes in the law. Statutory, regulatory and common law changes should be reviewed on an ongoing basis to ensure that health agency policy is consistent with legal requirements.

9

Computerization and Information Linkage

INTRODUCTION

The health field is enamoured with electronic technology, and particularly with the computer. Computer technology provides intensive care monitoring, computerized laboratory analysis, CT scans, fluoroscopy, MRIs, computerized assisted interpretation of ECGs, foetal monitoring, electronic health records and data storage. Transmissions occur via computer fax, e-mail, videoconference, telehealth, Intranet, local area networks (LAN), Internet and soon via the SuperNet and involve one-person offices to provincewide and nationwide databases.

Provincial initiatives such as Alberta Wellnet have developed computer databases, such as the Seniors Drug Profile and Pharmaceutical Information Network (PIN), Telehealth, as well as initiatives such as newborn metabolic screening program, breast screening program, cervical cancer screening program, integrated cancer network, pathology lab results, lab test history, provincial personal health identifier and SPHINX.[1]

The electronic health record is defined by the Canadian Health Record Association as:

> A computer-based patient record is an electronic patient record that resides in a system specifically designed to support users by providing accessibility to complete and accurate data, alerts, reminders, clinical decision support systems, links to medical knowledge, and other aids.[2]

Proponents of computerized health information and information linkage, say that computers will facilitate communication of health information and improve care.

---

[1]   Alberta Wellnet, *Progress Report*, April 2001-June 2001.
[2]   Canadian Health Record Association, "What is a Health Record?" online: CHRA <http://www.chra.ca/what/index.htm>, quoted from the *Institute of Medicine (IOM) Report*, 1990.

The Corporation, incorporated by Health Canada as part of Infoway Canada, has $500 million in federal funding to expedite the development of the electronic health record on a Pan-Canadian basis.[3] The extent of connectivity will depend upon whether consistent health information and data standards are adopted by users for managing and exchanging health data, such as in the initiatives underway at the Canadian Institute for Health Information (CIHI).

Many provincial initiatives for electronic health records exist, but successful initiatives require attention to numerous soft aspects including change management.[4] The Physician Office System Program (POSP) in Alberta is a funding mechanism where Alberta Health and Wellness provides substantial funding assistance to physicians who wish to move to an electronic health record.[5] These office information systems provide physicians with choices of scheduling software, billing software, access to medication, laboratory and imaging reports, clinical knowledge tools, electronic health records, Internet connectivity and e-mail.[6]

From a legal point of view there is uncertainty about computerized health information. This is due in part to the lack of judicial precedent and recent amendments to existing legislation. However, at least three legal issues are of concern to both lawyers and health professionals. These are:

(1)   confidentiality, privacy and security of computerized health information;
(2)   substandard practices for computerized information; and
(3)   use and disclosure of computerized information in court.

These issues are particularly important in the context of health information linkage, databases and Smartcards. Application service providers (ASPs) store data in remote locations, far away from the office or facility. In the past, health information was restricted to the place in which it was physically stored whether it was a hospital, clinic, doctor's office, laboratory or nursing home. The information moved from one location to another only if someone physically moved it.

---

[3]   *Pathways to Better Health*, Health Canada, 1999, Tactical Plan, P/T/F (Provincial/Territorial/Federal) Advisory Committee to the Council of Deputy Ministers, Advisory Council on Health Infostructure, Health Canada; W. Pascal, "Sharing the Wealth for Better Health", Health Care Information Management and Communications, March 2002, 1st Quarter, Vol. XVI No. 1, at 39.

[4]   B. Haver, "HER and the Rule of 'Ate'", Health Care Information Management and Communications, March 2002, 1st Quarter, Vol. XVI, No. 1, at 28.

[5]   J. Dyck, "The Case For Change — Physician Office System Program", *Alberta Doctor's Digest*, May/June 2002, Vol. 27, No. 3, at 25.

[6]   Alberta Medical Association, "Getting Wired With Confidence", *Alberta Doctor's Digest*, March/April 2002, at 6; the Alberta Medical Association sponsors two conferences on information management/information technology each year.

Information Linkage

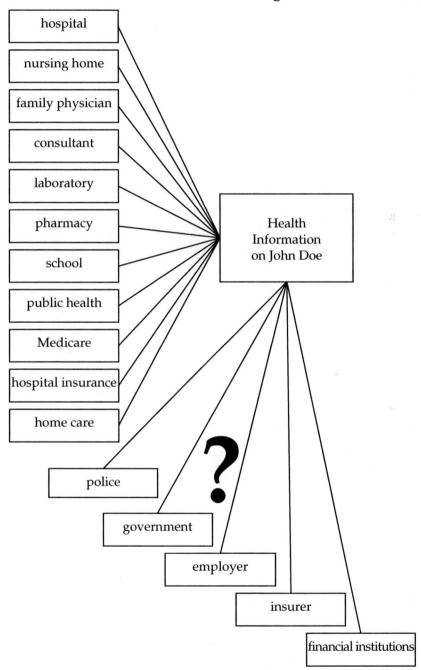

   With computerization the information may be quickly retrieved. With linkage of computer systems at each health facility, the information may be moved from one location to another with speed and with far less effort, depending upon the linkage or connectivity of the computer terminals. There is increasing pressure from patients and providers to utilize technologies such as e-mail and the Internet for the provision of health services, notwithstanding privacy and security concerns.[7]

   The advantage to the individual can be enormous. The client's physician does not have to wait for laboratory reports since they would be available on the terminal in his or her private office, which would be linked to that of the laboratory. The emergency department would not be treating an unconscious person "blindly" since with an identification number, the past history of hospitalization, medical care and allergies would be known immediately. Valuable time and lives would be saved. However, the legal problems that were previously confined to physical documentation kept in one place are intensified as the "location" of the information can conceivably stretch across the country and abroad.

CONFIDENTIALITY, PRIVACY AND SECURITY WITH COMPUTER INFORMATION

Confidentiality, privacy and security for electronic information is recognized in some provincial statutes.[8] The *Personal Health Information Act* in Manitoba requires a trustee who maintains health information in electronic form to implement additional safeguards including security safeguards.[9] The *Health Information Protection Act* in Saskatchewan enables an individual to require a trustee not to store a record on a networked electronic health record and requires a trustee that has entered into an agreement with the Saskatchewan Health Information Network (SHIN) to inform individuals about the agreement.[10]

   Under the *Health Information Act* in Alberta a custodian must obtain consent to disclosure by electronic means before information can be disclosed.[11] Before a custodian conducts data matching, precautions such as

---

[7]   N. Stuart, "Healthcare: The New Economy's Last Frontier?", *Healthcare Management Forum*, Autumn 2001, Vol. 14, No. 3, at 49; D. Protti, "The Increasing Reality of Using the Internet for Electronic Health Records", *Healthcare Management Forum*, Autumn 2001, Vol. 14, No. 3, at 4.

[8]   Canadian Institutes of Health Research, "Electronic Records and Data Linkage" in *A Compendium of Canadian Legislation Respecting the Protection of Personal Information in Health Research*, April 2000, at 8.0 – 8.5.

[9]   S.M. 1997, c. 51 (C.C.S.M. c. P33.5), s. 18(3).

[10] S.S. 1999, c. H-0.021; s. 8.

[11] R.S.A. 2000, c. H-5, s. 59.

a privacy impact assessment and notification of the Commissioner may be required.[12]

As a general rule, health information is not to be disclosed without consent or legal authority. However, there are exceptions to privacy that erode this right. Permission to review electronic health information may be granted to researchers, to a coroner or others. Provincial health insurance programes require health information. For more detailed discussion see Chapter 8 — Confidentiality, Privacy and Disclosure to Third Parties.

Computerization of health information has the potential to compromise confidentiality and privacy. More people may have access to a computer file than to a conventional handwritten chart. Information linkage has the effect of compounding the problem by increasing the amount of information available. There is the danger of curious staff and hackers gaining unauthorized access to personal information. Hackers can disrupt the provision of care that is dependent on computerized monitoring and information.

Without safeguards and security there may be little that is confidential. There is nothing to guarantee against negligent breach of confidential computer-based health information data. Safeguards and security measures can be developed by skilled computer specialists. Unique identifiers, biometrics, access codes, and rotating lists of identifiers are but a few examples. Computerized information can be more secure than hard copy records but if there is a breach, the breach could be due to the ready access to large volumes of data. Staff education is required on the importance of confidentiality and the serious consequences of a breach.

Health information managers should not wait for provincial legislatures to act before setting safety standards. Existing legislation was drafted with handwritten records in mind. It may take some time before revised legislation is put in place. Even new legislation may be technology neutral. Confidentiality and privacy standards should be set well in advance of installing a computerized health information system. The advice of information technology staff and legal counsel should be obtained so that technology and law may be taken into account when drafting policies, procedures, standards, contracts and privacy impact assessments and when integrating appropriate security standards.

In the setting of standards and procedures particular reference should be made to professional guidelines such as the *Position Statement on Security of Computerized Health Information* of the Canadian Health Record Association (CHRA).[13] The CHRA standard recognizes the individual's right to privacy and the need to protect the information from loss or un-

---

[12] *Ibid.*, ss. 69-72.

[13] Canadian Health Record Association, *Position Statement on Security of Computerized Health Information* (Don Mills, Ontario: CHRA, 1989).

warranted access. At the same time it recognizes the need for the authorized personnel to have relative ease of access. The Canadian Council on Health Services Accreditation (CCHSA) sets the standard in this regard by requiring that staff, service providers, clients, and families have access to information to support decision making and to improve knowledge.[14]

The CCHSA states that the CHRA *Position Statement on Patient Access to Health Records*[15] applies equally to computerized and hard copy information. The CHRA includes position statement recommendations for health facility policies and procedures regarding security of computerized health information. The CCHSA sets standards requiring confidentiality, privacy and security, which do not make a distinction between computerized information and other health information. The health organization has the duty to protect the confidentiality, security and integrity of data and information.[16]

SUBSTANDARD PRACTICES

A crucial issue in computerization of health information and information linkage is negligence. The concern involves improper use and improper recording of information. Because of the ease of creating and storing information in a computer as compared to writing it out manually, errors may be made more easily.

Failure to include information or recording information in an improper fashion resulting in injury to an individual would be cause for litigation. The same would be true of negligent linkage of computerized information resulting in physical harm. Failure to read physician's orders, misreading orders, clicking on the wrong drop-down box, tardy entries of laboratory results, typographical errors in entering vital signs or drug dosages, entries in the wrong record and faulty transmittal of patient history on record linkage are but a few of the possible opportunities for error.

For a health facility to be found negligent in these circumstances implies that standards exist for the entry and use of computerized health information. The standards will come from those who establish and operate computerized systems. For example, Canada's Health Informatics

---

[14] CCHSA, *Information Management*, ss. 3.0 and 5.0.

[15] Canadian Health Record Association, *Position Statement on Patient Access to Health Records* (Don Mills, ON: CHRA, 1985). See also Canadian Health Record Association, *Principles and Guidelines for Access to and Release of Health Information* (Don Mills, Ontario: CHRA, 1995).

[16] *Information Management, supra*, n. 14, ss. 7.0 and 8.0.

Association (COACH) Guidelines[17] are well recognized and provide a variety of standards for different settings. For large sophisticated facilities the International Standards Association (ISO) standards may be applicable. The guidelines should not be set at an unreasonably high level nor should the minimum threshold be too low. If the standards are set at an inadequate level, the court may impose its own minimal requirements and make a finding of negligence.

Negligence can also arise from improper storage and reliance on computerized health information. For example, if there is inadequate disaster recovery and files are not backed up regularly and the system crashes resulting in the loss of important data, the inability of caregivers to provide average, reasonable, prudent care could lead to a lawsuit. Without hard copy or electronic back-up, a major system crash could cause havoc, with staff "guessing" at necessary treatment orders, when medications were last administered or are supposed to be given to patients or residents.

Negligence may also arise if the off-site back-up system is not maintained properly. If located in a flood plain, and waters submerge the system, the inability to call up health data could lead to injury to individuals or residents. The failure to adequately respond to warnings about computer "worms" or "viruses" may also be grounds for negligence. If a health agency or provider knows or should know that it is at risk of a system failure due to a computer virus in its programs and does not take appropriate action, subsequent systems failure resulting in injury to patients or residents could set negligence litigation in motion.

Liability may also arise from the negligent failure to respond to known system limitations or to have appropriate manual back-up methods in place. For example, a nursing home pharmacist finds that a drug interaction screening procedure is not working properly but fails to call the software company for technical support to rectify the problem. The pharmacist goes off duty and the next pharmacist, unaware of the problem, relies on the screening procedure. The message sent back after processing the medication requisition is to proceed.

However, due to the flaw in the software, a drug interaction problem is not detected. As a consequence, the resident experiences a severe drug reaction and dies. It could be argued that the knowledge of the first pharmacist vicariously put the agency on "notice" and the failure to take corrective measures resulting in reasonably foreseeable injury is grounds for negligence. The pharmacist would be personally accountable as would the employer.

---

[17] Canada's Health Informatics Association (COACH), *Guidelines for the Protection of Health Information*, 2001.

Since down-times or system crashes can reasonably be anticipated, health agencies and providers must have in place manual or electronic back-up procedures to assure continuity in charting and care. The failure to have these systems in place can lead to havoc and can result in allegations of negligence due to injury to patients, residents, clients, and in some cases to visitors and staff. The best approach is to "test" manual back-up procedures and system on a periodic basis and to make certain that staff receives regular in-service education.

Growing reliance on computerized assisted interpretation of health information may result in undue reliance to the exclusion of the more traditional evaluation by a skilled clinician. If it can be shown that injury resulted from the failure to use known computer information, the stage could be set for negligence.

Staff must recognize the need for diligence in using computerized information in a proper manner, and to recognize the limitations of computerized health information systems. A system must be established to insure that practices are followed; otherwise legal difficulties can occur. Particular attention must be paid to computer and industry standards including COACH, ISO and CCHSA standards that require the health organization to collect and report data and information that is relevant, in a way that is timely, efficient, accurate and complete.

This approach applies to all collection and recording methods whether by paper or by computer.[18] The entire information system must also be comprehensive and integrated.[19] For example, failure to abide by accreditation standards, especially in an accredited facility may be considered as evidence of negligence.

DISCLOSURE OF COMPUTERIZED INFORMATION

Proper use and disclosure of computerized information requires appropriate controls over who can obtain data. This is particularly important if data is stored on a mainframe that can be easily accessed externally by someone from a different department or facility. This is even more important when data is stored in a remote location such as by an ASP vendor or where the database contains a large amount of data such as in a provincial or national database. The PIN in Alberta and PharmaNet in British Columbia are examples of provincial databases.

The basic ground rules that govern access to hard copy information apply to computerized files. This means that health agencies should have policies and procedures in place that address the following:

---

[18] *Information Management, supra.,* no. 14, s. 3.0.
[19] *Information Management, supra.,* no. 14, s. 4.0.

- Who will be permitted access? Will students doing a practicum in the agency or will researchers be granted the opportunity to obtain data? If so, will there be any restrictions imposed? Will they have to pass a training or orientation program? What about medical residents and interns or new members of the professional staff? Will government and public agencies within the same government or from different governments have access, and if so, for what purpose? Will access be limited and only on a need-to-know basis?
- Will staff be assigned passkeys or entry codes? If codes, will they be changed on a regular basis? What will be the anticipated response of the agency when a staff member reports that a wallet was stolen along with an entry code? Will periodic penetration tests be done to identify inadequate security measures?
- Will some data require higher level security and additional passkeys or entry codes? With regard to sensitive data, including information about child or spousal abuse, AIDS, drug addiction and mental illness, will only restricted designated personnel be granted computer file access?
- How will corrections and new information be recorded in the computerized files? If an error is detected in the computerized file, how should the error be corrected? If information comes to light that is important for individual care that is out of sequence, how will this fact be noted in the computer file record?
- Will abbreviations be permitted? If so, which abbreviations will be recognized as acceptable data entry?
- Will Smartcards and other electronic devices be used? Will specific interface requirements be required? How will caregivers be able to determine whether the data on a Smartcard is current and accurate?
- How will community pharmacy online information of prescription drugs interface with physician, hospital, nursing home, home care, office practice and Internet information?
- If an individual requests access, amendment or correction of a computerized entry how will this be handled? Will a separate "challenge file" be added? What happens if the caregiver who made the entry refuses to amend or correct the entry? How will such matters be addressed?
- Will periodic audits, penetration tests and privacy risk threat assessments be conducted? Will the results be utilized to improve practices for protecting confidentiality , privacy and security?
- Will a privacy impact assessment (PIA) be conducted to review and assess risks at both the corporate and the project level? Will

an internal multidisciplinary team work together to complete the PIA, or will the PIA be contracted out of the organization?

These issues and related concerns should be anticipated in agency-wide policies and procedures governing access to computerized records. Having basic "problem-solving" or trouble-shooting incorporated into established policies and procedures can lessen staff anxiety regarding the use of computerized information. Well-established information technology and information management system routines can help reduce the likelihood of injury stemming from deficiencies in computerized health information.

COMPUTERIZED INFORMATION IN COURT

There are a number of potential legal problems that are associated with computerized health information as evidence in court. Of particular interest are admissibility in evidence and credibility (see also Chapter 6 — Health Information as Evidence). All provinces have now passed electronic transactions acts pursuant to the Uniform Law Conference of Canada initiative[20] to harmonize this type of legislation across Canada.

Many provinces are now amending their provincial evidence acts to incorporate these new provisions.[21] For example, the *Electronic Transactions Act* in Alberta[22] has received Royal Assent, and when proclaimed will be incorporated into the *Alberta Evidence Act*.[23] There are various types of electronic evidence including e-mail, word processing documents, historical computer data, databases and storage media. Other electronic evidence exists in devices such as fax machines that keep electronic records of faxes, photocopiers, access cards, cell phones and personal digital assistants such as palm pilots.[24]

---

[20] See Uniform Law Conference of Canada, *Uniform Electronic Evidence Act*, online: ULCC <http://www.ulcc.ca>; K. Chasse, "Electronic Evidence: Computer-Generated Records in Court Proceedings" (Uniform Law Conference of Canada: Proceedings of the 1994 Annual Meeting), Appendix J; similar provisions to the provincial initiatives exist in the *Personal Information Protection and Electronic Documents Act (PIPEDA)*, S.C. 2000, c. 5, in force as of May 7, 2000.

[21] S. Johnson, "Evidential and Practical Issues with Electronic Evidence" (Canadian Bar Association Conference, Alberta Branch, Mid-Winter Meeting, 25 January 2002); R. McDonald, "Electronic Evidence — Tips and Traps for Litigators" (Canadian Bar Association Conference, Alberta Branch, Mid-Winter Meeting, 25 January 2002).

[22] S.A. 2001, c. E-5.5, s. 33, Royal Assent but not yet proclaimed.

[23] R.S.A. 2000, c. A-18.

[24] R. McDonald, *supra*, n. 21, at 5-8.

Part of the purpose of the electronic transactions acts is to establish a clear and certain procedure for admission of electronic records into evidence. The *Alberta Evidence Act* has two prerequisites for the admissibility of an electronic record into evidence, which are authentication and satisfying the best evidence rule. The authentication component means that the record is what it purports to be, a step, which is also required for hard copy documentary evidence at common law.[25]

The best evidence rule relates to the integrity of the electronic records system, which is usually addressed using a computer generated printout of the electronic record to establish the integrity of the electronic records system.[26] The best evidence rule using hard copy documents at common law involved the original document being admissible rather than a copy or secondary evidence.

One of the difficulties with an electronic record is determining whether the original is the record stored in the computer or rather is the computer generated printout of that record, or whether both are originals.[27] The amendments to the *Alberta Evidence Act* raise issues about inconsistency with the *Alberta Rules of Court* provisions for authenticity of records[28] and for filing an expert report to establish the integrity of an electronic records system.[29] Work is under way to develop a national standard for e-evidence under the Canadian General Standards Board (CGSB). The standard has just been released for public viewing and comment before being released as the official national standard in Canada.[30]

Most provincial evidence acts broadly define a business record. For example, in Nova Scotia "record" includes any information that is recorded or stored by means of any device.[31] The *Evidence Act* in Manitoba is similar.[32] The term "any device" is broad enough in scope to include computerized client records. The question remains, however, whether other aspects of the laws of evidence are met.

---

[25] *Alberta Evidence Act, supra,* n. 23, s. 41.3, as amended by the *Electronic Transactions Act, supra,* n. 22.

[26] *Alberta Evidence Act, supra.,* n. 23, s. 41.4, as amended by the *Electronic Transactions Act, supra.,* n. 22.

[27] S. Johnson, "Evidential and Practical Issues with Electronic Evidence", *supra,* n. 21, at 5-7.

[28] *Alberta Rules of Court,* Rule 192(1)(a).

[29] *Ibid.,* Rule 218.1.

[30] Electronic Records as Documentary Evidence — CAN/CGSB-72.34, released for review and comment, June 2002; past standards include the Microfilm and Electronic Images as Documentary Evidence-CAN/CGSB 72.11.99, developed in 1993.

[31] S.N.S. 1989, c. 154, s. 23(1).

[32] R.S.M. 1987, c. E150, s. 49(1).

To be admissible in evidence, a recording must be made in the "usual and ordinary course"[33] of a health facility's daily activities so computerized entries must be a commonplace occurrence. Moreover, to be admissible in evidence the entry must be made at or within a reasonable time after care has been provided.[34] The same would apply to laboratory tests or x-rays.

In using computerized health information in court it would have to be shown that it is customary for health information to be stored in this manner. It requires evidence that the system employed with reference to the individual in a particular lawsuit was the same that is generally used. This can be accomplished through the testimony of a health record administrator.

Proving that an entry was made at or near the time that care was provided should not be too difficult to establish. The computer can be programmed to automatically enter the time and date of each entry or to require the insertion of such information as part of an access code.

The laws on what is required for admissibility of documentary evidence vary from jurisdiction to jurisdiction. There are still questions about whether computerized health information is admissible as evidence. With proof of customary use of computerized health information and contemporaneous entries, such information should be admissible in court. There remain, however, problems relating to credibility.

Many of the provincial laws note that the circumstances surrounding the making of a record affect its weight or importance but not its admissibility in evidence.[35] Under these laws judges are entitled to place greater emphasis on some evidence than others. Given the number of people who have actual or potential access to computerized health information, the weight and credibility attached to such evidence may vary.

If it can be shown that changes can be made to a computer entry long afterwards without leaving an audit trail or indication of who made an amendment and when, the information may be discredited. If alterations were made and nothing was included in the information to designate a modification, the computerized information may be given little if any weight. This may have an adverse impact on the court regarding the credibility and veracity of the health facility's side of the case.

As noted in the previous section, to avoid such allegations, a health agency should adopt and enforce a policy regarding the correction of errors and the amendment of information. The policy should follow much the same practice as for handwritten records. (See Chapter 18 —

---

[33]   *Ibid.*, s. 49(2).
[34]   *Ibid.*
[35]   *Ibid.*, s. 49(4).

Prototype Policies and Procedures.) The time, date and name of the person should be included along with a brief explanation for the alteration and where the correct entry may be found. With computers, it can be inserted immediately after the incorrect entry. The original entry should remain intact although designated as no longer in force, for example, by a flashing on and off on the monitor screen.

To prevent allegations of tampering or the possibility of tampering, the system should be designed to eliminate as much of this hazard as possible. Special memory destruction codes could be programmed into the computer to prevent accidental or purposeful record changes. Opportunity could be built into the program for modifications, but only after access has been provided through a restricted code known only to administrative personnel. Staff would have to justify their reasons for changing health information. This could be assessed in terms of a predetermined set of criteria. Health information protection systems should be brought out in evidence if the suggestion is raised that the health agency, its employees or staff physicians could alter the record.

In addition, it is important that all health facilities have a method by which the authorship or validity of a statement, order, document, report, or records by an electronic means, which replaces the handwritten signature of the author or writer, can be established. Specific guidelines have been issued by the Canadian Health Record Association in its position statement and recommendations on the subject.[36]

THE FUTURE

Computerized health information still has a long way to go before it gains universal acceptance in health facilities in Canada. Access codes, built-in devices to prevent breaches of privacy, information entry and handling, error correction programs, manual back-up systems, staff training programs, and information linkage require careful thought before computers are put online. The evolution of Smartcards and voice recognition technologies may speed up this process.

From a legal point of view, it is important to seek out qualified legal advice on the collection, use, disclosure, storage and destruction of computerized data. Litigation is but one potential use. Research, vital statistics, risk management, utilization management, TQM/CQI, quality assurance, peer review and credentialing are other considerations.

Evidence acts should be reviewed carefully to determine if in fact business records or health records are defined broadly enough to include

---

[36] *Electronic Authentication* (Don Mills, Ont.: CHRA, 1994).

computerized health records. Other applicable legislation and regulations should also be examined. If there is any doubt as to the legality of computerized records, such information systems should not be used.

Ordinarily, it is not always the best policy to seek comprehensive legislation in setting up new forms of information handling. Legislators may react before there is anything to react to on a given subject. Some may be determined to have legislation recognizing the legality of computerized health information. Having laws relating to computerized health information runs the risk of non-experts setting standards that may be inappropriate and difficult to change. It seems preferable for the computer experts to set their own practical standards and put their policies into operation before provincial legislation is imposed. Various legislative developments have occurred and will continue to evolve.

Electronic transactions acts have paved the way for electronic commerce with a digital signature recognized in the place of a traditional one. Technology is working toward a generally available electronic signature. The replacement of physical documentation with electronic or computerized health information and universal health information linkage is just beginning. The law should be a reflection of society and health practice, not lead the way.

10

Faxes and Health Information

While a few years ago facsimile (or fax) machines were the latest and most exciting development in the transmission of health information, faxes have begun to fade in significance as computers, palm pilots and e-mail take the limelight. However, faxes are still with us, and continue to raise issues in sending and receiving health information.

The fax machine permits rapid-fire transmission of critical information that can facilitate quality health care. An image of the hard copy document is made in the sending fax machine and a replica of the document arrives at the receiving fax machine. Fax transmissions usually involve communications sent over ordinary telephone lines. However, faxes can now also be sent directly through a computer terminal.

Much of the concern focuses on confidentiality of the health information being faxed. There are also concerns about consent for transmitting health information via fax and the storage and destruction of faxed copies. Questions also arise about the admissibility in legal proceedings of faxed materials in place of the originals.

Some of these concerns are purely a matter of speculation, but they exist nevertheless. Many concerns may be lessened with clearly written policies and procedures as well as staff education. The key is to recognize that risk factors do exist and that preventive measures can diminish the chances of litigation. For this reason the Canadian Health Record Association (CHRA) in its position statement requires all health care facilities to establish policies and procedures specific to the transmission of health information by fax.[1]

CONFIDENTIALITY AND FAX TRANSMISSIONS

Confidentiality and privacy of health information has become of paramount legal importance. Confidentiality is dealt with in a Canadian

---

[1] Canadian Health Record Association, *Transmission of Health Information by Facsimile (FAX)* (Don Mills, Ont.: CHRA, 1989), Position Statement, s. 6.

Health Record Association position statement.[2] Standards of the Canadian Council on Health Services Accreditation (CCHSA) require health organizations to protect the confidentiality, security and integrity of data and information.[3]

Privacy Commissioners in Ontario and British Columbia have published guidelines for transmitting personal information by fax, which includes health information.[4] Public bodies such as regional health authorities, provincial boards and ministries of health must incorporate such guidelines in fax policies and procedures. Professional colleges have developed guidelines for when health professionals can utilize fax transmissions to provide specific health services, such as when a faxed prescription can be used for dispensing a medication.[5]

A simple slip of the finger on the numeric keypad can result in the wrong party receiving a highly confidential fax transmission. In many instances, the recipient may be more annoyed than interested in the contents of the errant transmission. However, the same cannot be said of highly sensitive business transactions or personal health care information.

Sending a fax transmission to the wrong party constitutes a breach of confidentiality. For some individuals the indiscretion can prove highly damaging, particularly if the contents of the transmission deal with sexually transmitted diseases, mental illness or physical conditions, which may be perceived as detrimental.

A breach of privacy occurred recently when a fax from a social worker at Alberta Hospital Edmonton was mistakenly sent to the *Edmonton Journal* rather than to a hostel. The social worker was attempting to make discharge arrangements, so the fax included detailed patient information including name, address, date of birth, hospital number, contact persons, psychiatric and personal history. The social worker had followed procedure, but accidentally inverted a "6" into a "9" when she typed in the fax number. The Privacy Commissioner determined this to be a situation of human error.[6] This example shows the importance of caution when transmitting information by fax.

---

2   *Ibid.*
3   *Information Management Standards* (Ottawa: CCHSA), s. 7.0.
4   A. Cavoukian, *Guidelines on Facsimile Transmission Security* (Information and Privacy Commissioner, Ontario, February 1999); *Guidelines for the Secure Transmission of Personal Information by Fax* (Office of the British Columbia Information and Privacy Commissioner, August 1996).
5   See *e.g.*, College of Physicians and Surgeons of Alberta, "Facsimile Transmission of Prescriptions", CPSA Guideline, March 1999.
6   Investigation Report 2001-IR-003, Alberta Mental Health Board, Alberta Information and Privacy Commissioner, May 17, 2001.

The chance that a fax can go to the wrong dedicated line is not insignificant. Indeed, even if a fax is sent to the "right" telephone number, the opportunity exits for breach of confidentiality. For example, the recipient may have the fax machine situated in a high traffic area or in a location that is not secure or not monitored.

Hospital emergency departments are a good illustration in point. High volumes of traffic pass through the area each day. Busy staff may not notice an unauthorized person reading through fax transmissions. The same can be said of half-hearted attempts at protection involving placement of the fax machine in a "discreet" location totally insulated from routine security monitoring. Once again, unauthorized persons could help themselves to fax transmissions.

The CHRA Position Statement requires that a fax from one health care facility to another be sent from and received in the health record department.[7] In small facilities health record departments as such may not exist, as in a physician's office. However, the transmission should take place between staff with responsibility and control for health records.

NEGLIGENCE ISSUES WITH FAX TRANSMISSIONS

Aside from negligent breach of confidentiality, there are other issues involving substandard practices involving faxed information. Consider four examples:

1. *Failure to check for results of stat or urgent tests in a reasonable period of time.* If a "stat" order is placed by fax that involves a specific turnaround time, and the normal waiting period is exceeded, the failure to follow up could constitute substandard practice. It could be argued that staff know or ought to know that after a given time interval, it is important to follow up. The failure to do so, resulting in foreseeable harm or death would constitute negligence. The Canadian Health Record Association recommends that health information should only be transmitted by fax when required for urgent or emergent care.[8]

2. *Negligent transcription of faxed information.* Health care agency policy may require that faxed data be transcribed into the treatment record. Errors in transcription or the failure to make transcriptions in a timely manner are substandard care. Where it can be shown that as a reasonably foreseeable consequence of such

---

[7] *Supra*, n. 1, s. 3.
[8] *Ibid.*, s. 2.

substandard care an individual was injured, the groundwork
would be in place for a negligence lawsuit.

3. *Negligent failure to read the faxed information.* Liability may arise
    as a result of a caregiver failing to read faxed information usu-
    ally considered in the care and treatment of patients, nursing
    home residents or home care clients. The failure to use the in-
    formation or the failure to use it in a timely manner, resulting in
    foreseeable injury or death, could constitute negligent practice.

4. *Relying on illegible transmission copy.* Sometimes faxed transmis-
    sions are illegible, pages are missing or sometimes the docu-
    ments overlap and obscure a portion of a page. The result is the
    same: the recipient cannot totally comprehend the content of the
    intended information. The failure to call the sender and request
    a retransmission or clarification would be substandard practice,
    particularly if the recipient chose to make an educated "guess".
    Any foreseeable injury resulting from this behaviour could con-
    stitute grounds for negligence.

There are many other illustrations of possible negligence stemming
from improper use of fax transmissions. The key is to establish a clear-
cut policy on the use of fax equipment and properly process the documents. This is the best protection against the possibility of negligence
arising from the use of fax machines.

THE CASE FOR SECURING CONSENT

The question is often asked: should health care professionals or health
care agencies obtain consent for use of fax transmissions in the treatment
of patients, residents, or clients? Lawyers are not in agreement, suggest-
ing that it is best to secure individual legal advice on the matter.

The CHRA, in its position statement on the use of fax transmissions
suggests that any form of authorization for the release of health information transmitted by fax is acceptable. The only conditions are that the
original authorization must be sent to the health care facility in hard
copy such as by mail and that the authorization must meet all criteria for
validity.[9]

Some believe that health care providers should inform patients, residents and others about the "risks" associated with fax transmissions of
personal health care information. This would include the chance that
wrong telephone numbers will be accessed and that even if the correct

---

[9]   *Ibid.*, s. 5.

number is dialed, there is a chance that unauthorized individuals at the other end of the line will see the information and use it improperly.

Others believe that this type of advice is too conservative and will actually scare off individuals for whom rapid transmission of such data would facilitate care. Furthermore, they argue that this is not really part of the mainstream of informed consent to "treatment".

There is a middle ground in the debate. It is appropriate that individuals understand that their health care records will be transmitted via fax in order to facilitate quality care. Individuals should understand that the caregiver originating the transmission cannot guarantee complete confidentiality of the data once sent via fax. Once told of these facts, some individuals may be understandably reluctant to permit such fax transmissions. Whatever the individual decides should be noted in the health record along with an indication that the use of fax was explained.

Some health care agencies and providers may go a step further and require the individual to sign a consent authorizing transmission by fax. This is a decision that health care providers must make in light of specific legal advice.

ADMISSIBILITY OF FAX TRANSMISSIONS

Fax transmissions are considered part of the health record if placed in the chart. Lawyers can attack the genuineness of a faxed document as well as the genuineness of other components of the health record.

Problems can arise if health care agencies do not place the actual fax in the record, but a photocopy of the document. Thermal paper fax printouts fade over time so photocopies on bond paper may be prepared.

These concerns can be obviated by developing and following a consistent approach for copying thermal paper fax printouts that meet the requirements of a "business record". The process would have to show:

(1) the documentation is copied in a manner that demonstrates it is a true and authentic reproduction; and
(2) the procedure is done in a usual and customary manner with all similar fax copy paper.

Guidance should be obtained from legal counsel who provide specific recommendations to meet applicable evidence act and court rules of procedure governing the reproduction of original documents. In addition, it would be prudent to discuss the matter with experts in health record administration or information management. (See Chapter 6 – Health Information as Evidence)

RETAINING AND DESTROYING FAX TRANSMISSIONS

If a faxed transmission is incorporated into the health record, the rules governing retention and destruction of the chart apply. This basic principle applies with regard to institutional records, community health care charts and physician office-based patient documentation. The requirements of applicable legislation and regulations must be taken into account as well as the purposes for which the records are maintained.

Retention and destruction concerns become more complex when a photocopy rather than the original faxed communication is incorporated into the health record. Although some are concerned that the copy will have less evidentiary weight, this need not be the case. If, as noted above, a policy and procedure is implemented and followed for making a copy of the document, it should be treated as a business record. This is particularly so if the photocopy in question was prepared following the usual and customary practice. It may be necessary to photocopy faxed documents from fax machines that do not use bond paper, as this precludes long term storage.

Other retention issues may arise as there may be more than one attempt to fax the information. The fax may be followed by the original being received in the mail. The documents may have information that has been added such as the date received and notations indicating who has read the document and when information was communicated.

Fax copy destruction is a serious issue. Fax copy can accumulate in a busy unit, such as the emergency department. Copies left intact can be read by unauthorized personnel or used to the detriment of an individual.

Health care agencies and facilities should recognize the security implications of unneeded fax copy and develop a practical approach for proper destruction of these documents. Such a policy should contemplate the following:

1. Who determines which documents are to be destroyed?
2. Who is authorized to destroy the documents?
3. What are the acceptable methods for destroying unneeded faxed copy?
4. How frequently should destruction occur?
5. Will the documents be destroyed on location or will the paper be transported to another location for this purpose?
6. What kind of quality management process will be used to make certain that the documentation is destroyed in accordance with policy and procedure?

Whatever methods are used, staff must understand the importance of properly disposing of unneeded faxed communications. Until the information is destroyed, the need for maintaining confidentiality is a prime consideration that should be addressed by selecting an efficient, cost-effective process.[10]

PRACTICAL RULES FOR FAX TRANSMISSIONS

The CHRA has developed a cogent position statement and a series of recommendations for faxed health information.[11] The CHRA recommendations include suggestions on equipment acquisition, machine security, dialing accuracy, careful screening of documents to be faxed, advice on photocopying faxed transmissions and the steps to follow when transmitting information.[12] These excellent points are incorporated along with risk management-oriented recommendations in what can be used as a practical checklist for faxed transmission of health information as follows.

PRACTICAL RULES FOR FAX MACHINES IN HEALTH CARE

1. *Select proper equipment.* Make certain the equipment includes state-of-the-art security functions such as passwords, keylocks and pre-programming of telephone numbers.[13] Technological safeguards such as confidential mailboxes and encryption should be considered.[14] When possible, select fax machines that use bond paper so faxes do not need to be photocopied for longevity.

2. *Make certain staff understand how and when to use the fax.* Orientation and in-service education programs should be used to train staff in the proper means of using the fax machine. Training should also reinforce when the fax machine should and should not be used as a means of communicating health information. This is important for assuring confidentiality and proper utilization of the device.

3. *Ensure that individuals are advised or agree to personal information being faxed.* Patients, long term care residents, and community care clients should be told why faxed transmissions are used in

---

[10] For further discussion of destruction of faxed health information, see J. Barrack, "An RM Approach to Avoiding Fax Pitfalls", *RRM Report*, Vol. 3, No. 3, June, 1991.

[11] *Supra*, n. 1.

[12] *Ibid.*

[13] *Ibid.* See also J. Barrack, *supra*, n. 10.

[14] *Supra*, n. 4.

their care as well as the possible risks. This explanation should include the possibilities of errant transmission and lack of maintaining confidentiality by those receiving the data. The fact that the individual has been informed and either agrees or disagrees with the use of the fax should be noted in the health record. It should be made clear if exceptions will be made for exigent situations such as "stat" requisitions for blood matching or blood gases in the emergency department.

4. *Locate the fax in a secure place.* Place the fax machine in a secure location, which is monitored regularly. This step helps to discourage unauthorized personnel from using the machine or attempting to "read" confidential fax copy.[15] When possible, adopt the technology that allows faxes to be sent directly via computer lines to the intended work station.

5. *Develop a permissible transmission policy.* Categorize the various types of information and develop a list of the types of information or records that can be transmitted by fax. Make certain that the list is not ambiguous.[16]

6. *Develop a tickler follow-up system.* Make certain that faxed requisitions are screened for required follow-up. This is especially important when important diagnostic test results are expected. Once a requisition is "flagged" as being outstanding, appropriate steps should be initiated to obtain the requested information.

7. *Develop a policy on fax documents being copied.* Make certain that the policy governing photocopied fax documents takes into account the prospect of the information being used in court or other legal proceedings.[17]

8. *Develop a policy on retention and destruction of fax documents.* Make certain that a clear-cut, but practical policy is in place governing the retention and destruction of fax information. Take into consideration limitation periods, multiple copies and the various purposes for which the documentation is used. Make the destruction procedure effective and consistent.[18]

9. *Use an effective transmitting procedure.* The following is the procedure recommended by CHRA:

    •   the receiver shall be notified by telephone that the information is being transmitted
    •   the receiver shall stand by to receive the information

---

[15]   *Supra*, n. 1.
[16]   *Ibid*.
[17]   *Ibid*.
[18]   J. Barrack, *supra*, n. 10.

- the sender shall transmit a covering letter to accompany the health information. The letter shall contain the following:
    - name, address, and phone number of the sender
    - name, address, and fax number of the receiving party
    - number of pages transmitted
    - a notice that the following information is confidential
- the sender shall seek confirmation of receipt of the transmission[19]

10. *Implement risk management and quality management monitoring techniques.* Monitor on an ongoing basis for problems associated with faxed transmission of health record information, including the following:
    - unauthorized transmission
    - failure to use transmitted information
    - illegible transmissions relied upon and inappropriate care or injury resulting
    - failure to follow up on requisitions beyond outlier dates
    - frequency of "wrong" numbers dialed
    - confidentiality breached
    - failure to obtain patient authorization for or to advise patients about fax transmission
    - inappropriate routing of faxed information
    - unauthorized access to faxed information
    - unnecessary reliance on faxed communication

Use the data generated from the monitoring system to improve the communication process, to safeguard health record confidentiality and to improve care.

---

[19] *Supra*, n. 1.

11

Documenting Treatment Orders

THE PHYSICIAN'S ROLE

Despite the trend toward multi-disciplinary care, physicians remain the key decision makers for treatment and care. Physicians diagnose patients or residents and determine the course of medical treatment. Physicians have the primary authority to admit, transfer and discharge patients in hospital. A resident may need to be under the care of a physician to be admitted to a long term care facility.

Medical treatment is provided by the attending physician as well as by other medical specialists or consultants requested by the attending physician. The physician utilizes the advice and assistance of many other groups of health care professionals such as nurses, occupational therapists, respiratory therapists and dieticians.

Other health care professionals make numerous judgments independent from physicians. For example, nurses independently provide a wide range of interventions including monitoring and care such as routine vital signs. Physicians can order a broader range of vital signs or more frequent vital signs on an individual basis but are entitled to expect nurses to take routine vital signs. Physicians usually determine whether other clinical services are to be utilized and specific steps taken such as laboratory and diagnostic imagining tests.

Health professionals such as psychologists, optometrists, chiropractors and dentists have traditionally worked independently from physicians. Delegated practice legislation has created further exceptions to the general rule. Health professionals such as dentists, pharmacists,[1] podiatrists,[2] optometrists,[3] midwives and nurses[4] now have authority to diagnose,

---

[1] See *e.g.*, Alberta College of Pharmacists, "Prescribing by Pharmacists", *ACP News*, May/June 2002, at 4.

[2] See *e.g.*, "Podiatrists Prescribing Authority", *College of Pharmacists of British Columbia Bulletin*, May/June 2000, Vol. 25, No. 3, at 3. In B.C. podiatrists can prescribe drugs pursuant to the *Pharmacists, Pharmacy Operations and Drug Scheduling Act*, except for narcotics and controlled drugs.

[3] See *e.g.*, "Optometrists Prescribing Limits", *College of Pharmacists of British Columbia Bulletin*, May/June 2000, Vol. 25, No. 3, at 3. In B.C. optometrists can prescribe two drugs (cyclopentolate and tropicamide) for use in their offices for diagnostic procedures.

[4] The *Registered Nurses Providing Extended Services Regulation* under the *Public Health Act* has authorized nurses who are listed under the *Nursing Profession Extended Practice Ros-*

treat and refer in certain circumstances and jurisdictions. However, certain decisions such as prescribing narcotics have remained within the exclusive practice of physicians.[5] Nurses may be the first and only contact in the school, occupational health clinic, family planning clinic or in an isolated rural area. The same is true for primary caregivers in home care settings.

TREATMENT ORDERS

"Treatment orders" may be written or verbal, and may be individual or standing orders. "Physician's orders" may be given in general terms such as "for physiotherapy" or "dietary assessment" or may specifically outline what treatment or task is to be done such as to book a particular type of surgery.

Physicians are responsible for writing physician's orders. Traditionally medical orders have been located on physician's orders forms on a separate page in the health record. A recent trend is a movement towards treatment orders, which are multi-disciplinary orders of physicians and others with authority to write orders. Treatment orders are now often combined with progress notes that include recommendations and observations about the response to treatment.

Treatment orders have legal and professional implications. Health professionals acting beyond their area of authority may be subject to professional discipline for "professional misconduct". A recent example occurred in Alberta where a nurse was disciplined for administering a medication without a doctor's order.[6] Every order is part of the service provided and affects the care or treatment. The legal principles relating to services provided to a patient, long term care resident or home care client apply equally to physician orders.

Two major legal issues arising from medical orders relate to satisfying standards of care and meeting requirements of evidence. The standard of care issue arises when a patient sues the physician, nurses and facility for negligence alleging that the medical order was given negligently, was communicated improperly, was transcribed incorrectly, was followed

---

ter Regulation to provide nurse practitioner services in Alberta since 1995. Alberta Association of Registered Nurses, *Prescribing and Distributing Guidelines for Registered Nurses in Advanced Nursing Practice Providing Primary Health Care Services,* January 1995 and re-endorsed February 2000; Alberta Association of Registered Nurses, *Competencies for Registered Nurses Providing Extended Health Services in the Province of Alberta,* December 1995.

[5] Only health professionals such as physicians who are defined as a "practitioner" in the federal *Controlled Drugs and Substances Act* can prescribe narcotics and controlled drugs.

[6] Alberta Association of Registered Nurses, "Discipline Decisions", *Alberta RN,* April 2002, Vol. 58, No. 4, at 15.

incorrectly or perhaps was not followed at all. (See Chapter 4 — Standards for Health Information.)

The issue of evidence arises when one party or the other attempts to prove that an order was given. There may be a question whether a physician actually gave a particular order. Was the order recorded as intended? Did the order mean what those following it thought it meant? If there is no written order, can the oral testimony of witnesses be accepted in its place?

In order to minimize these problems and minimize risk to the patient, written orders are preferred over verbal orders. Written orders provide more certainty for the person giving the order as well as for those carrying out the order. While errors do occur and legibility issues do arise, what is written is usually the same as that which is read. Verbal orders which are subsequently recorded could be altered from the order given due to misunderstanding or memory lapses between the time the order is given and recorded.

The result can be injury and a subsequent lawsuit alleging negligence. From an evidentiary point of view, it is easier to prove a written order recorded by the physician at the time rather than to prove a verbal order based upon the memory of someone trying to recall an event that occurred months or years previous.

VERBAL OR TELEPHONE ORDERS

It is recognized that occasions exist when written orders cannot be obtained such as by paramedics at the scene of an accident or by a code team in a hospital. There are times when a treatment order must be given verbally or over the telephone such as in emergencies. Health services that involve telephone advice such as telehealth and e-health are expanding rapidly. The improvement in access to health services is evident as clinical expertise such as psychiatry can be routinely brought to remote geographic areas.

A telephone order is merely one type of verbal order, which is communicated by voice. Increasing demand exists for communications by various electronic means other than the traditional handwritten communications of the past. Health professionals now routinely document and communicate using handheld palm pilots, laptops used at docking stations, e-mail, faxes and computer systems that include Intranets, the Internet and computer databases. Physicians now make notations about individuals when attending at the bedside, including the care that needs to be provided such as treatment orders.

Questions arise as to what words such as "written" and "signed" mean when using electronic means. Notations can be typed into a palm pilot or computer that are capable of being printed out in written form, but this is what has been traditionally regarded as a handwritten communication. Access to electronic devices may require a unique password and other security steps including biometric data such as fingerprints, but this is not what has been traditionally regarded as a signature.

Legislation has been enacted across Canada that recognizes electronic transactions as being equally as valid as written transactions. The technology does not yet exist to enable electronic signatures in health care, but this technology will no doubt be developed. Due to all the new electronic possibilities, on an interim basis health care facilities may need to establish clear guidelines about what is and is not recognized as being in writing or a signature in each facility. It would be ideal for these guidelines to be consistent across the health care system but this consensus may take some time.

Verbal treatment orders are typically recorded by the health professional receiving the order. Steps can be taken to minimize the risks that are inherent in verbal orders. A written record of a verbal order should be made immediately when the order is received. For example, pharmacists accepting verbal prescriptions must write out the prescription and date and sign the prescription[7] as required by regulations under the federal *Food and Drugs Act*.

When possible, the order should be repeated back to the person giving the order. If possible a second person should listen to the order and the order should be taken only by persons with appropriate training. The order should be signed as soon as possible thereafter. The circumstances under which a verbal order will be sought or given should be strictly limited.

Without a written notation by the person who gave the order, it is difficult to prove that a particular order was given. Even where the order is written immediately by the receiving person, the person who recorded the order may be accused of making a mistake and may bear responsibility for any injury caused by the error.

To further reduce the possibility of error, the person dictating the order should make a notation of the order to ensure that what is being read back is correct and is the same as what is later signed. However, where there is disagreement there is a risk of being accused of fabricating notes for self-protection.

Some health professionals feel that one way to minimize these concerns is to permit medical orders by fax or other electronic means. Communication of other types of orders such as prescriptions are now allowed by fax. This approach presumes that every agency and health professional has the

---

[7]   Alberta College of Pharmacists, "Recording Verbal Prescriptions", *ACP News*, May/June 2002, at 4.

technology for such electronic communications. Authentication and security are an issue as faxed and computer e-mail messages could be sent by someone other than a physician. The likelihood of an imposter sending these messages can be reduced with security features such as access codes and the likelihood of the information getting into the wrong hands can be reduced with security features such as encryption. Health facilities will need to consider these issues and formulate guidelines that address the new technologies.

Vicarious diagnosis is another source of concern. Much information is gained by direct observation. This risk arises when health services are provided based on telephone communications such as in emergency departments, telephone consultation and telehealth initiatives. When health care professionals rely on second hand information from other caregivers or family members, they are taking a chance with the well-being of the patient or nursing home resident. If the observer emphasizes one observation or does not mention another observation the result may be an inappropriate treatment order.

The result of inadequate communication could be injury or death for the patient or resident. The end product may be a finger-pointing exercise between the health professional and the first-hand observer who conveyed impressions over the telephone. Standard protocols and questions are of great assistance to ensure a consistent and comprehensive approach. These communications including the advice given should be documented. Advances in e-health that enable direct observation such as teleconferencing will be of great assistance when widely available.

Deterrents should be in place to discourage inappropriate reliance on verbal and telephone orders. Chart abstracting could identify questionable or unnecessary verbal orders or unsigned orders that are flagged and scrutinized by a clinical review team. The intent should not be to single out the "bad apple", but to improve overall performance. However if a pattern of inappropriate verbal orders continues for a particular individual, then disciplinary action is an option to be considered. This could mean alteration of health facility privileges.

Another approach may be to create in health care agency policy and procedure a rebuttable presumption that a telephone order which is dictated, repeated back to the person giving the order, and recorded immediately by the person taking the call, will be presumed correct as charted. This decreases the likelihood of nurses being left "holding the bag" for persons who, after the patient or resident has suffered an adverse consequence, assert that the telephone order was not transcribed accurately. Under this approach, the order is presumed correct as written in the health care record unless evidence can be produced to the contrary. Knowing that such a policy exists could be a deterrent to undue reliance on verbal orders.

Advances in technology may create increased acceptance of non-written or verbal orders. Pharmacists in some jurisdictions now accept prescriptions recorded by prescribers on the pharmacy voicemail system.[8] Voice recognition technologies are still in early development but with improvement in this technology some of the current difficulties with verbal orders will by overcome.

STANDING ORDERS

Medical orders usually apply to an individual patient or a long term care resident. These directives are unique to the circumstances of the individual being treated. However, physicians or departments may also issue "standing orders" to be applied in the treatment of particular types of patients or patients of a particular physician or area. These orders go into effect for individuals without the signature of a person issuing the order.

Standing orders are invaluable in emergency situations such as for resuscitative measures initiated by code teams and paramedics when time is of the essence and before individual physicians are available. Standing orders have been influenced by the movement toward consistency in health services evident in clinical practice guidelines and best practices for a variety of situations. In some instances, standing orders will actually improve the standard of care provided by practitioners who are outliers compared to their peers.

Routine stop orders can be regarded as a type of standing order where medication orders automatically stop after a prescribed time, for safety reasons. Stop orders for particular medications are typically formulated by hospital committees involving pharmacists, physicians and other staff. When a stop order applies, physicians must renew medication orders to continue the medication. An example arises under the Alberta legislation, which provides that hospital by-laws must provide for routine stop orders on antibiotics, narcotics, anticoagulants, sedatives and other potentially dangerous drugs.[9]

Standing orders are sometimes not placed on the health care record but are incorporated by reference for example in public health programs that involve immunizations. Most agencies require standing orders to be included in the record. Standing orders may be stamped onto the physician's order sheet. Standing orders provide a standardized "cookie-cutter" approach to treatment that permits little flexibility for individual

---

[8] See *e.g.*, "Verbal Prescriptions on Voicemail", *College of Pharmacists of British Columbia Bulletin*, May/June 2000, Vol. 25, No. 3, at 3; Alberta College of Pharmacists, "Recording Verbal Prescriptions", *ACP News*, May/June 2002, at 4.

[9] *Operation of Approved Hospitals Act Regulation*, Alta. Reg. 247/90, s. 16.

needs. With standing orders the care provided to patients, nursing home residents and home care clients is governed by a predetermined set of instructions.

Consider a post-partum patient who has undergone an episiotomy. Once in her room, the doctor writes in the chart, "Standing Orders". This triggers a pre-set list of nursing actions as well as provision of 222s for pain. The order does not take into account the fact that the patient has a severe allergy to aspirin: acetyl-salicylic acid (ASA).

Proponents will argue that the risk of the patient receiving the drug will be averted by the fact that her chart will have been marked with a warning label regarding the ASA allergy. While the allergy may be documented elsewhere on the chart, it is possible that busy staff will not read the chart carefully enough or will not associate the ASA allergy with 222s. It is even more likely that staff will miss cross-sensitivity problems such as the additional allergies that can be anticipated with known allergies such as penicillin and will merely proceed to carry out the standing order.

Standing orders have been the subject of much criticism. The Canadian Council on Health Services Accreditation (CCHSA) has attempted to eliminate the use of standing orders in the past. However, standing orders are still in use in Canadian health facilities but now certain steps must be taken including review and approval in accordance with specified criteria. For example, standing orders must be within the area of competence of facility staff and medication orders must state the medication name, route, frequency and duration and provide individual dosages where possible.[10]

There is a question regarding the quality of care provided when standing orders are permitted. It is essential that staff is more vigilant in identifying individual needs and challenging orders when using standing orders. Writing individualized treatment orders does take time, but writing the order requires consideration of the needs of each patient. The same can be said for nursing home residents and home care clients. The same types of criticisms can be directed at other caregivers who fall into the trap of relying on standing orders as an administrative convenience.

From risk management and quality care perspectives, as a general rule standing orders are discouraged. Reducing the risk of possible injury and better care planning are positive gains which stem from reducing reliance on standing orders. The extra time required to write treatment orders can be offset through improved chart design and training on effective charting methods. The electronic health record will expedite the

---

[10] See *e.g.*, "Standing Medication Orders", *College of Pharmacists of British Columbia Bulletin*, May/June 1999, Vol. 24, No. 3, at 6.

writing of treatment orders and may even assist in selecting treatments of choice, for example by highlighting drug incompatibilities.

CHALLENGING TREATMENT ORDERS

Staff may disagree with treatment orders on occasion. Sometimes it is a matter of a nurse questioning the orders of a physician. In other cases it may be a health care professional such as a medical resident questioning the treatment orders written by another physician. Challenging treatment orders is particularly important when using standing orders or verbal orders due to the risk of error in those situations.

The issue of questioning or challenging a treatment order has become pronounced in recent years, particularly as health care professionals recognize their high level of responsibility for improper treatment. Staff is no longer placated by suggestions that they need not worry because the employer will "cover them".

Often the individual whose order requires clarification or is questioned, appreciates the inquiry. The question provides a degree of comfort that patients or residents are not being given hands-on care by staff who blindly carries out orders.

In other situations, the person who gave the order becomes quite upset. Defensive, hostile, and sometimes verbally abusive, the person remains adamant in having the order fulfilled. Unless the health care agency has a system in place for handling such matters, safety and quality care may be in jeopardy.

An effective means for handling these matters is a so-called "challenged order" policy and procedure. Such a policy applies to all caregivers. It is premised on good faith efforts to maintain quality care through a businesslike approach to resolving concerns stemming from treatment orders. The challenge policy follows a step-by-step approach:

1. The caregiver identifies a treatment order which is deemed inappropriate based upon professional judgment.
2. The person who made the order is contacted. The nature of the concern is conveyed with a request for clarification.
3. If the person who challenged is satisfied with the explanation, the matter ends. However, if the individual is still concerned, this fact must be conveyed to the person who made the order.
4. If the person who made the order remains firm, the challenge is quickly transferred to the department head or a designate for resolution.
5. The department head or designate makes a determination after reviewing the record and circumstances of the case. The person

who made the treatment order may also be contacted to discuss the matter.

6. If an alternate treatment order is made by the department head or a designate, the new order is recorded in the health record in accordance with the agency's policy and procedure.

7. There is no reprisal against the person who challenges an order unless the challenge was made maliciously or was not made in good faith.

8. Each challenge is recorded along with the resolution in appropriate administrative documentation designed for the purpose such as incident reporting.

9. Caregiver-linked challenge profiles are reviewed for purposes of performance appraisal or medical staff credentialing, whichever is appropriate.

10. Corrective action is taken in the form of training or alteration of staff privileges in appropriate cases.

The overall intent is not to single out one individual for disciplinary action. Rather, the intent is to maintain and improve the quality of care. However, if it becomes evident that the practices of a particular caregiver are woefully inadequate, the data gathered can be used to take remedial action. In the case of doctors or other health professionals with hospital privileges, this could mean alteration of privileges.

LEGISLATION AND BY-LAWS

Health sector legislation and facility and medical staff by-laws typically prescribe the process for granting privileges and accompanying rights such as the authority to admit, treat and discharge patients. Different categories of staff have different privileges as some staff will have only treatment privileges while other staff will also have admitting privileges. Some staff will have carte blanche authority for treatment orders while other staff will have restrictions.

Some jurisdictions have specific legislative requirements for physician's orders that require treatment orders to be written, dated and signed. In Ontario, a procedure for verbal orders has been prescribed in the regulations under the *Public Hospitals Act*[11] and is thus imposed by law on all public hospitals in that province. This regulation[12] states:

---

[11] R.S.O. 1990, c. P.40.
[12] R.R.O. 1990, Reg. 965.

(1) Every order for treatment or for a diagnostic procedure of a patient shall, except as provided in subsection (2), be in writing and shall
   (a) In the case of an order for treatment be dated and authenticated by the physician, dentist or midwife giving the order, and
   (b) In the case of an order for a diagnostic procedure be dated and authenticated by the physician, dentist, midwife or registered nurse in the extended class giving the order.
(2) A physician, dentist or midwife may dictate an order for treatment or for a diagnostic procedure by telephone to a person designated by the administrator to take such orders and a registered nurse in the extended class may dictate an order for a diagnostic procedure by telephone to any such person.
(3) When an order for treatment or for a diagnostic procedure has been dictated by telephone,
   (a) the person to whom the order was dictated shall transcribe the order, the name of the physician, dentist, midwife or registered nurse in the extended class who dictated the order, the date and time of receiving the order and shall authenticate the transcription; and,
   (b) the physician, dentist, midwife or registered nurse in the extended class who dictated the order shall authenticate the order on the first visit to the hospital after dictating the order.[13]

Similar provisions exist in other provinces with some variations.[14]

In Alberta an order is regarded as being in writing if the order is dictated to a nurse or authorized person, signed by that person on behalf of the dictating physician and countersigned by the physician within 24 hours.[15] A similar provision applies to long term care except the order must be countersigned by the physician on the next attendance at the facility.[16]

Even in the absence of legislation for treatment orders, health care facilities or agencies may impose requirements through by-laws, policies and procedures.

---

[13] *Ibid.*, s. 11.

[14] See *e.g.*, B.C. Reg. 121/97, ss. 5, 11, 12; *Private Hospitals Regulation*, Man. Reg. 58/93, ss. 1, 2; *Care Facilities Regulation*, Man. Reg. 337/88, ss. 47, 49; *Operation of Approved Hospitals Act Regulation*, Alta. Reg. 247/90, ss. 9, 14; *Nursing Homes Operation Regulation*, Alta. Reg. 258/85, ss. 19, 20; *Hospitals Act Regulation*, N.S. Reg. 16/79, s. 16(a)-(h); N.B. Reg. 92-84, s. 18; N.B. Reg. 84-212, s. 36; R.R.N.W.T. 1990, c. I-6, ss. 83, 87; *Hospital Management Regulations*, P.E.I. Reg. EC 574/76, ss. 30, 35; R.R.O. 1990, Reg. 937, ss. 3, 7; O. Reg. 57/92, s. 10; *Hospital Standards Regulation*, Sask. Reg. 331/79, s. 17.

[15] *Operation of Approved Hospitals Act Regulation*, Alta. Reg. 247/90, s. 14.

[16] *Nursing Homes Operation Regulation*, Alta. Reg. 258/85, s. 19.

PRACTICAL RULES FOR TREATMENT ORDERS

1. *Authority to Write Treatment Orders* — Health care facilities and agencies should formulate guidelines regarding which individuals or categories of staff have authority to write treatment orders and clearly describe any limits to this authority. This is particularly important for new categories of health professionals and students such as medical residents with the authority to give treatment orders.
2. *Verbal Orders* — Health care facilities and agencies should develop policies and procedures that clarify the specific circumstances when verbal or telephone orders are acceptable and the steps that must be taken to minimize the risk of error. Facilities need to determine whether orders will be accepted by electronic means and if so what constitutes a "written" order and a signature.
3. *Standing Orders* — Health care facilities and agencies should develop policies and procedures that clearly set out the specific circumstances where standing orders are acceptable and when stop orders will be imposed. Staff needs to be reminded to be particularly vigilant to identify individual needs that might not be met with standing orders.
4. *Challenged Orders* — Health care facilities and agencies should consider whether to develop a policy and procedure for dealing with challenged orders. Staff needs to be reminded that verbal orders and standing orders have a higher risk of error and need to be challenged where safety concerns arise.
5. *Legislative Review* — Health care facilities and agencies should ensure that statutes, regulations and by-laws and professional practice standards in their jurisdiction are reviewed on an ongoing basis and ensure that policies and procedures for treatment orders are consistent.

12

Documenting Health Information

One of the most common questions in health information is the style of documentation. Is problem-oriented charting the best format? Should our health care agency move away from a particular method of recording? Do we need flow charts? Should we record on fetal monitoring strips or electroencephalogram (EEG) tracings? What type of intraoperative charting is best? How detailed does discharge planning need to be? Can we document part of all of the information electronically? What about using palm pilots and laptops to document at the point of care?

There is no simple answer to what is the best or the worst method of recording health services. Much depends on the needs of the agency and the type of service being provided. However, there are some basic principles to bear in mind when deciding on the style and content of forms and methods used for documenting treatment.

PRACTICAL CONSIDERATIONS

1. *Review Purposes.* As indicated earlier (Chapter 2 — Purposes of Health Information), there are many reasons for documenting health information. The ability of the agency to support clinical treatment is of prime importance. Therefore, in deciding what should or should not be included under the rubric of documenting "care" or "treatment", the fundamental purposes of health information must be considered.

2. *Current Approach.* Do the various forms and methods currently in use in the agency provide an accurate, easily accessible picture of the health services provided? Do the records contain too little or too much information? Does the reader have to comb through the chart in order to find out what is going on? If the current method of documenting treatment is efficient and effective, it may be best not to change it at all. However, if there is room for improvement, dit is prudent to identify the ways in which the current approach should be modified.

3. *Care Providers.* Sometimes forms and information systems are designed with one professional group in mind. The fact that the format is awkward or inappropriate for another group is not taken into consideration. Indeed, there may be no common ground for the different groups to voice their concerns. The disadvantaged group may only do the "bare bones" charting requirements or they may develop a parallel documentation method. In either instance there is risk of communication failure and poor patient care. Therefore, in deciding which method of documenting is best it is imperative to canvass all key stakeholders and incorporate ideas about what will and what will not work.

4. *Quality Management.* As noted in Chapter 17 — Risk Management in Health Information, major changes are underway in health management to support quality care. These changes include variations on traditional quality assurance, risk management, utilization management, program evaluation, and total quality management/continuous quality improvement (TQM/CQI). Whatever framework is utilized, it is imperative that the system for recording health services is compatible with these initiatives. The documentation must provide accurate information to enable appropriate quality management decisions to be made. Hence, quality management initiatives must be considered when determining the best approach for documenting health services.

5. *Consistency.* Communication breakdowns may arise due to inconsistencies in policy and procedure charting requirements. Inconsistencies can exist for many aspects of charting such as vital signs, abbreviations, and the propriety of "tracings" (EEG, ECG, or fetal monitoring strips) being included in the treatment record. The best approach is a consistent perspective. Thus two general nursing units in the same agency should follow the same format in terms of recording vital signs. Making certain that a consistent policy is translated into action requires a review of education policies and procedures and staff training. Patients transferred between units could be victims of an inconsistent approach. Staff may make the inference that the lack of entries in the transferred patient's record means that all is well. However, this may only be a different style of recording in the other unit and a source of miscommunication about patient status.

6. *Pre-admission and Discharge Planning.* Pre-admission and discharge planning are major concerns for health facilities and agencies due to shorter lengths of stay and higher patient acuity.

Working with numerous community-based agencies, patients and families can be a daunting responsibility. Explicit instructions are essential. Financial cutbacks may compound the difficulties. The result may be excellent documented admission and discharge planning on one shift and poor recording on another. Instructions should be clear and understandable to enable adequate preliminary and discharge care. In multilingual regions or where illiteracy is a concern, particular care must be taken to ensure that information and instruction sheets are understandable.

7.   *Multi-disciplinary Approach.* Rather than forms cropping up in an *ad hoc* fashion, it is prudent for the health care agency to have one group serve as the forum for health information initiatives. In the past this group was referred to as a "Forms Committee". Now a multidisciplinary task force typically has a similar task, but with a broader focus on health information and informatics. Health information has achieved a significant profile and it is not uncommon to have such a group reporting to the Chief Information Officer. The purpose of the group is to develop a user-friendly and efficient documentation method that works for all caregivers. The group needs to solicit the input of the end-user, including doctors, nurses, social workers, utilization managers, record abstractors, information managers, information technologists and recipients of care. Legal counsel should review proposed forms and methods to ensure consistency with applicable law and defence in possible legal proceedings.

8.   *Ongoing Intervention.* Once a set of forms or new system is developed and approved, it is imperative to conduct a pilot to identify and resolve problem areas. Once in full use, the documentation should be evaluated carefully on an ongoing basis, making certain that it fulfills the needs of recording health services in a timely, effective and accurate manner. As further needs for change are identified, appropriate modifications should be made to maintain quality care.

13

Documenting Consent

A fundamental principle of law in any civilized society is that no one may interfere with the body of another person without that person's consent. This principle is found in many legal systems. Under the civil law system of the Province of Quebec, the *Civil Code* says:

> Art. 10. Every person is inviolable and is entitled to the integrity of his person. Except in cases provided for by law, no one may interfere with his person without his free and enlightened consent.[1]

In the English Common Law system of the other provinces and the territories, the courts have established the same principle.[2] While the application of the principle may vary among Common Law jurisdictions, such as England, Australia and the United States, the principle remains the same, even though the application may differ.

The diagnosis, care and treatment of an individual almost always involves interference in some way with the person's body, either directly by hand, or indirectly through medical devices, electronic means or medication.

So that this interference with the patient does not constitute an infringement of the patient's legal right to be free from interference, and thus be considered assault and battery, the patient must give what is known as a voluntary informed consent to the interference. The only other way, in which the interference can take place without infringing the patient's legal right to be untouched, is by having legislation specifically authorize the interference without consent.

There are two types of legislation, which fall into this category. The best known is that which authorizes compulsory hospitalization and treatment in certain cases of mental illness, usually when a person is a danger to himself or others. The second authorizes compulsory treatment or vaccination in cases of certain communicable diseases. Both types of

---

[1] Art. 10 C.C.Q.
[2] See *e.g.*, *Mallette v. Shulman* (1987), 43 C.C.L.T. 62, 63 O.R. (2d) 243, 47 D.L.R. (4th) 18 (H.C.J.), affd. (1990), 72 O.R. (2d) 417, 2 C.C.L.T. (2d) 1, 67 D.L.R. (4th) 321, 37 O.A.C. 281.

legislation are provincial and therefore, differ to a certain extent from province to province. All however, have built-in safeguards to limit what is a major interference with a person's liberty and right to be free from being touched by others.

Because statutory exceptions and voluntary consent are exceptions to basic legal freedoms, courts will limit the loss of this right as much as possible. It is extremely important therefore, that the rules, which govern a valid informed consent and the requirements of compulsory treatment legislation, be followed precisely.

If the question arises as to whether medical interference was legally valid, evidence will be required to show that an exception applied and was carried out correctly. This evidence is invariably documentary and becomes part of the health information package. This evidence is vital for the defence of any lawsuit to show that the bodily interference was legally permitted.

Relating to the consent exception, it is a fundamental principle that consent to treatment is a process, not a form.[3] It is part of the communications process in which caregivers and those to whom they offer treatment exchange essential information that results in a decision and an agreement regarding the care. Some degree of documentation of this transaction is necessary. This provides not only an historical record, but provides a check to make certain that the treatment provided is that to which the parties agreed.

LEGISLATIVE REQUIREMENTS FOR CONSENT DOCUMENTATION

Some jurisdictions in Canada have enacted legislation or regulations specifying the requirements for recording consent to treatment.[4] Much of the legislative activity focuses on hospital care. However, consent documentation requirements can also be found in other types of legislation. For example, the Nova Scotia *Medical Consent Act* specifies that the person giving a power of attorney for purposes of health care must do so in writing.[5]

The Quebec *Civil Code* requires that consent to care that is not required by a person's state of health, to the alienation of a part of a person's

---

[3] See L.E. and F.A. Rozovsky, *The Canadian Law of Consent to Treatment* (Toronto: Butterworths, 1990), and F.A. Rozovsky, *Consent to Treatment: A Practical Guide*, 3rd ed. (Gaithersburg, MD: Aspen, 2000).

[4] See *e.g.*, P.E.I. *Hospital Management Regulations*, EC 574/76, s. 48; *Hospital Standards Regulations*, R.R.N.W.T. 1990, c. T-6, s. 71.

[5] R.S.N.S. 1989, c. 279.

body, or to an experiment shall be given in writing.[6] New Brunswick also requires that consent be given in writing prior to surgery.[7] The problem however, is not whether the consent is signed or not, but whether there is documentary evidence that the consent process has been fulfilled. Evidence that the patient has signed does nothing to prove that the patient gave a valid and informed consent, and that the criteria required for a valid consent have been fulfilled.

Even where the consent legislation does not require documented consent, it is important to have it so that there is evidence that the legislation was followed.[8]

THE PATIENT INFORMATION SHEET

A further alternative is to provide the patient with a printed information sheet or brochure outlining the details of everything, which the patient must be told under the laws of consent. This would include the nature of the proposed procedure, the risks and benefits, the risks of not undergoing the procedure, and the reasonable alternatives. The patient would sign an acknowledgment of having read the material, having had the opportunity to ask questions, and having consented to the procedure.

The problem with standard documents providing the basic information required for a valid consent is that the information required by one patient might be different from the information required by another. Standard risks of a particular procedure may be the same for all patients. However, individual health conditions and personal situations differ so it is possible that the risks for one patient are different from the risks for another patient undergoing the same procedure.

Standard information sheets and brochures frequently ignore the problem of providing information that is customized to meet the unique situation of each particular patient. Brochures and pamphlets could address specific situations by including a space for customization for individual patients.

The legal risk is that if the necessary modifications are not made in a printed document, or are made incorrectly, the patient may be misled. The result is that the document is not enabling what the law requires, that is, to adequately inform the patient so that a valid consent or refusal can be given.

---

[6] Art. 25 C.C.Q.
[7] *General Regulation Hospital Act*, N.B. Reg. 92-84, s. 41.
[8] See *e.g.*, *Medical Consent of Minors Act*, R.S.N.B. 1973, c. M-6.1.

THE PROBLEM WITH TRADITIONAL CONSENT DOCUMENTATION

The fact that a patient, client or long term care resident signed a treatment authorization does not mean that the consent process is complete. Unless legislation or case law creates an irrefutable presumption that a signed document is a valid authorization, a judge can look behind the documentation to see if the requirements of a valid consent process have been met.

Evidence that the patient did not understand the explanation provided, the patient could not understand the form because of illiteracy or lack of fluency in the language, or that the information provided on the form did not reflect the risks associated with the actual procedure performed, are all good illustrations of a basis for challenging the consent process. A boilerplate consent form full of uncompleted blanks may also raise questions about the validity of the consent process and the evidentiary weight to be accorded the documentation.

Consent litigation may come down to a question of weighing the credibility of individual witnesses. The persuasive parties are bound to win, particularly if supporting evidence substantiates their claim. This includes consent documentation.

Traditional consent documentation follows one of two distinct formats. The first involves a long, detailed explanation of a proposed diagnostic or surgical intervention. Specified in the form are the probable risks and benefits as well as the available treatment alternatives. The risks associated with refusing care are also included.

Patients are often presented with this so-called "long form" consent document at a time when they are unable to weigh the advantages and disadvantages of the proposed care. Individuals may be so distracted by the impending procedure that they do not absorb the details in the form. Furthermore, lawyers write many forms with a heavy emphasis on legal jargon. Often those written by health professionals are overly scientific. Few health care agencies "pilot" these documents before implementing the forms. Between the technical language and the failure to determine whether the form is understandable, the consent document is sometimes of little use and of questionable evidentiary value.

Critics of the long form consent argue that the details recorded in the document may dissuade prospective recipients of care. They claim the long forms are too generic, and do not provide sufficient leeway for risk or benefit factors that are unique to individuals. They rely instead on so-called "short form" consent documents, which indicate that "the risks, benefits and alternatives to the proposed treatment or diagnostic test have been explained to me".

The short form document does leave the onus on caregivers to explain the details to patients. However, it also places considerable reliance on memory, given the fact that five or six years may pass before a consent case reaches trial. By that stage, knowing what was explained to patients years before can devolve into a contest of memories. The outcome will boil down to whether the court believes the professional or the patient as to what was or was not divulged.

Traditional consent documentation is no longer sufficient. It does little to support continuity of quality patient care nor to serve as an effective tool in the defence of legal action. Options are emerging, which may decrease the importance of consent forms.

INNOVATIONS IN RECORDING CONSENT

Several techniques are now under active consideration as means of recording treatment authorizations. These include the following:

Contemporaneous Note in the Health Record. Some health care agencies and caregivers favour the use of contemporaneous entries in the health record as the primary means for charting consent to treatment. The practice is based on the theory that if individual caregivers chart the process in the record, it is a good indicator that the process of consent occurred as stated. Courts will likely give more weight to customized consent entries in the chart as compared to fill in the blank forms.

The contemporaneous consent entry in the chart is not without its critics. If entries emerge that follow a "cookie-cutter" approach and this fact is brought to light in court, the contemporaneous note takes on little significance. This issue can be addressed through practical in-service education.

Videotaped Consent. Some caregivers believe that videotaping the consent process is the strongest defence tool available with which to defend a claim based on negligent consent. They believe that once a court sees how a patient responded to the consent process on tape, there will be little doubt about the adequacy of the authorization for diagnostic tests or treatment.

This idea too, has its critics. Patients, knowing that they are being videotaped, may be reluctant to pose questions. Fearing that they will appear stupid or cowardly, they may be reluctant to opt for more traditional and less risk-prone treatment alternatives. It is possible that the presence of the video camera will distract and upset patients to the point that the taping diminishes the evidentiary value of recording the process. Furthermore, unless tapes are made and maintained in a usual and customary manner, it leaves open the possibility of a challenge to the evidentiary value.

Consent Checklist. Another approach is to provide caregivers with streamlined consent documentation that incorporates all requisite elements of the consent process. Proponents believe checklists can speed up the consent process and reduce the chance of poor documentation of treatment authorization. Failure to meet the required elements of the checklist can be used as a risk indicator and may serve as the basis for disciplinary action.

Opponents claim that checklists are a step backward. They believe that checklists are nothing more than a sophisticated update of the old boilerplate consent form. They are concerned that the exchange of information between caregiver and patient has less importance than a process using a completed form.

Notwithstanding the criticisms, the consent checklist has many virtues. It serves as a prompt to caregivers regarding responsibilities in the consent process. Further, if designed properly, the data abstracted from the forms provides an important picture on the quality of information provided to patients in the consent process.

Combination Special. Perhaps the best approach to documenting consent is a combination of traditional forms, adjunctive videotapes made available for patient education, one-to-one discussion with the caregiver, and well designed brochures that outline the nature, purpose, and indications for such treatment. The "combination special" is based on the idea that each contact with the patient regarding consent to treatment will be recorded in the chart. This creates a paper trail which, when done properly, demonstrates that caregivers met their obligations.

Whatever method is chosen, the key is to make certain that consent is routinely documented in a usual and customary manner. Most importantly, the documentation method should support the underlying premise of consent as a communication process.

THE DIFFICULT CASES

Examples of difficult cases include patients refusing care, distraught families making treatment choices for a loved one, and decisions at the end of life.

Patients Who Refuse Treatment. The right to refuse treatment is an important and fundamental principle recognized in Canadian law even if the refusal may result in death.[9] Documenting the decision to refuse care can take place when a patient decides to leave a health care agency against advice, at the time a caregiver explains treatment alternatives, or it can occur well in advance of a situation arising in which a concurrent

---

[9]   *B.(N.) v. Hotel-Dieu de Quebec* (1992), 86 D.L.R. (4th) 385, 69 C.C.C. (3d) 450 (Que. S.C.); *Fleming v. Reid* (1991), 82 D.L.R. (4th) 298, at 309-310 (Ont. C.A.).

treatment decision must be made by the patient. Refusal can also take place while the treatment or care is in progress.

Many lawyers recommend that health care agencies and health professionals secure an executed release form from patients leaving against advice. The idea is to have a documented record that the person was apprised of the risks of refusing care and the alternatives available for treatment. While this approach has some merit, it does not take into account the frustrations of emergency departments or long term care wards where it is impractical or impossible, to get individuals to sign a release. The patient may be in a drunken state or in shock from an injury so that the individual does not have capacity to execute a release form.

Another issue arises when patients decide to forego appropriate treatment. It is important that the decision is based on sufficient information for the person to make an effective choice. Documenting an "informed refusal" of care is imperative, particularly if patients subsequently sue claiming the decision not to undergo treatment was premised on inadequate information. Solid documentation can refute such claims. It is not enough for the document to state that the patient was informed of the risks. Ideally, the actual information should be included, which the patient will acknowledge in writing.

Jehovah's Witnesses and other groups refuse treatment for specific reasons. Documentation of such choices is often completed well in advance of an illness or injury necessitating treatment decisions. Caregivers argue that such choices are not well informed because these decisions were made without prior knowledge of salient information. This type of argument was specifically rejected in the well-known Ontario case of *Mallette v. Shulman.*[10] Living wills and durable powers of attorney are recognized in Canada along with the need for practical documentation of refusal of consent.

Dealing with Distraught Families. Making substitute treatment decisions for close friends or relatives can be a trying experience. When family members do not agree among themselves on the course of necessary treatment, problems are bound to occur. A comprehensive policy and procedure manual on consent should ensure that staff knows who to approach for decisions. Policies and procedures should incorporate applicable legislation and regulations.

End of Life Choices. Many health care providers fear criminal reprisal if they shut off a respirator or disconnect a naso-gastric tube, even pursuant to patient or family request. Since patients disconnected from life support are likely to die soon thereafter, staff also fears the prospect of civil litigation for wrongful death.

---

[10] (1990), 72 O.R. (2d) 417, 67 D.L.R. (4th) 321, 2 C.C.L.T. (2d) 1 (C.A.).

Ideally, Parliament should amend the *Criminal Code* of Canada to allow caregivers to give effect to treatment choices at the end of life. To minimize the risk of civil litigation all provinces have passed advance directives, health care directives or personal directives legislation, which recognize the right of individuals to refuse treatments, procedures and care even when refusal may result in death. This type of legislation allows the appointment of another person to act on their behalf.[11]

The document signed by the patient must be maintained as part of the health record so that wishes are known and accessible to staff and to enable directives to be followed when the need arises. Hospitals and long term care facilities should develop and implement their own "standard of practice" regarding documentation of treatment decisions at the end of life.

Treatment policies and procedures in this regard must contemplate several factors, including who can make decisions for others, the scope of these decisions, and how decisions can be modified or revoked.[12] In terms of documentation requirements, several factors should be addressed. For example:

1. How should staff respond to a living will, health care proxy or durable power of attorney that does not meet the criteria found in agency policy?

2. What process should be followed if a friend or relative of the individual claims that the documentation does not reflect the person's current attitude regarding resuscitation, artificial hydration or nutrition?

3. How will decisions refusing care for compromised neonates be recorded?

4. Is a note in the record "Do Not Resuscitate" considered sufficient for the agency or must there be a formal DNR order signed by the attending physician?

5. How should staff document a verbal modification or revocation of a living will?

6. Must a card refusing blood or blood products be signed by the patient? Is it sufficient that the card is on the person of the patient? Must staff obtain ancillary evidence that the individual is a devout Jehovah's Witness who adamantly refuses blood products?

---

[11] See *e.g.*, (Ontario) *Health Care Consent Act, 1996*, S.O. 1996, c. 2; (Newfoundland and Labrador) *Advance Health Care Directives Act*, R.S.N.L. 1995, c. A-4.1; (Alberta) *Personal Directives Act*, R.S.A. 2000, c. P-6.

[12] For further discussion on the topic, see, L.E. and F.A. Rozovsky, *The Canadian Law of Consent to Treatment* (Toronto: Butterworths Canada, 1990), Chapter 7.

7. How should agency staff respond to written statements or bracelets on an individual such as, "Do Not Hospitalize"?

8. How should staff respond to written statements or notations in transfer forms accompanying residents from long term care agencies that indicate, "Do Not Resuscitate, Palliative Care Only"?

9. What procedure should staff follow in fulfilling the written wishes of an individual to donate bone, skin, or organs at the time of death?

10. How should staff document efforts to get permission from relatives that a request was made to authorize organ donation? This is particularly important in jurisdictions like Nova Scotia, which require that such requests be made in specific cases.[13]

The practical realities of fulfilling requests to refuse treatment and the other so-called "difficult cases" should be anticipated by health care agencies. Knowing these concerns exist should motivate health care agencies to develop practical approaches in consent policies, procedure manuals and consent forms.

Documenting HIV Testing. The social stigma of AIDS or HIV testing has led to innovative techniques for documenting permission for diagnostic tests. Some have even attempted to circumvent the issue by arguing that general hospital admission consent "covers" HIV testing.

The issue of recording permission for HIV testing should be discussed with legal counsel. The position taken by the health care agency should be consistent with the general requirements for recording consent. Provincial legislation must be taken into account. The end result should be a balanced approach that addresses legal requirements as well as the needs of the person undergoing HIV testing.

CONSENT FOR DISCLOSURE OF INFORMATION

Although the disclosure of health information will be generally discussed in more detail elsewhere (Chapter 8 — Confidentiality, Privacy and Disclosure to Third Parties), consent for disclosure of health information will be briefly covered here. Health information legislation authorizes the use or disclosure of health information in accordance with either statutory exemptions or with consent.[14]

---

[13] *Human Tissue Gift Act*, S.N.S. 1991, c. 13, s. 6A(1).

[14] See *e.g.*, *The Personal Health Information Act*, S.M. 1997, c. 51, ss. 21(b), 22(b); *Health Information Protection Act*, S.S. 1999, c. H-0.021, ss. 5, 27 (Note — enacted but not yet pro-

Some provincial health information legislation explicitly prescribes the criteria for this type of consent.[15] For example, the Alberta legislation says:

> 34(2) A consent referred to in subsection (1) must be provided in writing or electronically and must include
>
> (a) an authorization for the custodian to disclose the health information specified in the consent,
>
> (b) the purpose for which the health information may be disclosed,
>
> (c) the identity of the person to whom the health information may be disclosed,
>
> (d) an acknowledgment that the individual providing the consent has been made aware of the reasons why the health information is needed and the risks and benefits to the individual of consenting or refusing to consent,
>
> (e) the date the consent is effective and the date, if any, on which the consent expires, and
>
> (f) a statement that the consent may be revoked at any time by the individual providing it.
>
> (3) A disclosure of health information pursuant to this section must be carried out in accordance with the terms of the consent.
>
> (4) A revocation of consent must be provided in writing or electronically.
>
> (5) A consent or revocation of a consent that is provided in writing must be signed by the person providing it.
>
> (6) A consent or revocation of a consent that is provided electronically is valid only if it complies with the requirements set out in the regulations.[16]

The Saskatchewan statute sets out explicit criteria for consent to the collection, use or disclosure of health information.[17]

Health information legislation prescribes other specific situations where consent is required such as for the collection of health information by a device that may not be obvious like a camera[18] and the disclosure of health information for research.[19] The Saskatchewan legislation would give individuals the ability to opt out of having their health information stored on a networked electronic record.[20] In other jurisdictions, express

---

claimed); *Ontario Draft Privacy of Personal Information Act, 2002*, A Draft for Consultation, Part II; *Health Information Act*, R.S.A. 2000, c. H-5, s. 34(1).

[15] See *e.g.*, *Health Information Protection Act, supra*, n. 14, ss. 6, 27; *Ontario Draft Privacy of Personal Information Act, 2002, supra*, n. 14; *Health Information Act, supra*, n. 14, s. 34(2) – (6).

[16] *Health Information Act, supra*, n. 14, s. 34(2) – (6).

[17] *Health Information Protection Act, supra*, n. 14, s. 6.

[18] *Health Information Act, supra*, n. 14, s. 23.

[19] *Ibid.*, ss. 50(1)(a), 53(2)(b), 55; *The Personal Health Information Act, supra*, n. 14, s. 24.

[20] *Health Information Protection Act, supra*, n. 14, s. 8(1).

consent is required before health information can be disclosed by electronic means.[21]

PRACTICAL RULES FOR RECORDING CONSENT DECISIONS

There are many practical suggestions for recording consent decisions.[22] Record keeping and documentation should not prove unduly burdensome for caregivers, patients, residents or home care clients. Documentation should serve as a clear message of desired treatment and support quality and risk management techniques. Bearing these principles in mind, the following practical suggestions are provided to facilitate development of a good system for documenting consent:

1. *Develop a Comprehensive Consent Policy.* Make certain the policy and procedure addresses the requirements for consent, the recognized exceptions, and the way in which specific cases should be documented.

2. *Develop Necessary Consent Documents.* Streamline the consent documentation process. Do not create too many forms. Institute a system for practical consent documentation.

3. *Anticipate the Problem Cases.* Ensure that documentation strategies anticipate difficult situations such as refusal of care, withdrawal from treatment, do not resuscitate orders, do not hospitalize orders, organ donation, and leaving against advice.

4. *Document Ability to Consent.* Minimize challenges to consent on the basis of incapacity by including a mechanism in consent documentation for validating ability or authority to consent. This would take into account both legal and mental capacity to authorize or refuse consent to treatment.

5. *Research and Disclosure of Health Information Consents.* Be certain that documentation of consent for human research trials meets existing guidelines. Ensure that consent for disclosure of health information to third parties meets legal requirements.

6. *Provide Staff Training.* Make certain that staff receive orientation and in-service education on the proper way to document consent decisions. Ensure that staff demonstrates clinical competency in using the documentation process.

---

[21] *Ibid.*, s. 8(2); *Health Information Act, supra*, n. 14, s. 59.
[22] *Supra*, n. 12.

7.   *Monitor Consent Documentation.* Use health care agency systems for utilization, quality and risk management such as incident reporting. Identify and rectify problem areas.

14

Defamation

One of the most difficult legal questions raised with respect to health information is that of defamation. The difficulty derives from the fact that it concerns not only physical or economic loss, but the unquantifiably difficult loss of lessening of a person's reputation. The source of law in some provinces is wholly that of judicial precedent, whereas in others it is a mixture of common law and provincial statute.[1] In Quebec the basis is in the *Civil Code*.[2]

Canadian legal history is crowded with defamation suits. It is rare, however, to find a defamation suit arising from health information. This does not rule out such a possibility. Considering the increasing variety of health services being offered, the growing amount of information being collected and the increasing access to this information, it would not be surprising if there were more defamation suits. The well-developed legal principles in past defamation cases can easily be applied to health information.

A defamation suit could arise from one of four situations recorded in health records:

(1) a physician, nurse, psychologist, social worker or other staff member or consultant may make a comment in the record about a client which could be regarded as defamatory;

(2) a staff member may make a defamatory comment in the record about a third party, such as a member of the patient's family, or the patient's employer;

(3) the patient may have made a defamatory comment about a third party, and this is reported in the health records;

(4) a staff member may make a defamatory remark in a patient's health record about another staff member.

The comments that may be considered as defamatory may arise in the general recording of history, diagnostic remarks or nursing care. This is

---

[1] See *e.g.*, *Defamation Act*, R.S.A. 2000, c. D-7; *Defamation Act*, S.N. 1989, c. 122.
[2] Art. 1457 C.C.Q.

particularly true for alcoholic, drug abuse and AIDS patients. They are most likely to arise in psychological or social assessments of the client. The comments may also be made regarding the attitude or behaviour of the patient, client, resident, family or friends. Therefore, the records of mental health facilities, counseling services and long-term care facilities are more likely to contain defamatory statements than are the records of facilities and agencies caring for strictly physical ailments.

A wide range of statements may be interpreted as being defamatory such as comments about weight or appearance. These comments may be found in the records of any facility or agency such as in physicians' and nurses' notes, referrals and consultations, and notes made by numerous other staff members or consultants. These documents may contain statements about the attitude or conduct of a patient, family or friends, or remarks about the ability or attitude of health personnel. Any one of these situations may lead to an accusation of defamation of character and a lawsuit.

The questions that are commonly raised are:

(1) Can a health institution be successfully sued for defamation as a result of statements appearing in the health records?

(2) Can any individual making entries be sued successfully for defamation?

(3) Can the patient be liable for defamatory remarks made to a health professional who subsequently records the remark?

(4) Can the person who records a defamatory statement made by someone else or who distributes the file in which it appears be held responsible for defamation?

(5) Should certain information not be recorded since it might be defamatory?

(6) What are the defences to a defamation suit?

WHAT IS DEFAMATION?

A person commits the tort (or civil wrong) of defamation when the following factors are fulfilled:

(1) A false and derogatory statement is made respecting the plaintiff without lawful justification.[3] The reference must clearly be to the plaintiff.

---

[3]   *Church of Scientology of Toronto v. International News Distributing Co.* (1974), 4 O.R. (2d) 408, 48 D.L.R. (3d) 176 (H.C.). See *Pocket Dictionary of Canadian Law*, 2nd ed. (Toronto: Thomson Canada, 1995) at 145.

(2) The statement must affect the person's reputation and lower his character in the eyes of reasonable people, or possibly cause others to hate, shun or avoid that person.[4]

(3) Persons who claim they have been defamed must have a reputation to be defamed. They cannot complain about having lost either a reputation which they did not have or one which they deserve but did not have.[5]

(4) The statement must be "published". Publication of the statement is made simply by making it to one other person.[6] This can be in person, by telephone, telegram or letter. By placing a defamatory statement in a health record, it would be difficult to argue that this did not constitute publication. The purpose of placing information in the record is to have it read by others.

Anyone who "publishes" a defamatory statement can be held responsible for it, even if the statement did not originate with that person. The mere repetition of the statement cannot be justified merely by proving that it was a true report of what was said by somebody else. Using words such as "I was told" or "He said that" does not justify the defamatory statement. Therefore, the recording of a defamatory statement made by the patient or client is in itself defamation.

However, it is the publishing of a defamatory statement that constitutes the wrongful act and each person who repeats the statement is responsible.[7] Even though the person recording the defamatory statement in the record is doing so under orders, he is still held responsible.[8]

Whether a statement is defamatory or not does not depend on the meaning intended by the writer, but on what a reasonable reader or listener would think.[9] A statement that is an opinion can never be proved true. This is due to the fact that the person who made the statement says they have that opinion. The defendant can justify the statement by showing that the facts warrant such an opinion.[10]

The fact that a statement is vulgar or abusive does not make it defamatory unless the required elements of defamation are present. The fact that a statement is false does not in itself make it defamatory. Even words that hurt a person's feelings may not be defamatory.[11]

---

[4] A.M. Linden, *Canadian Tort Law*, 7th ed. (Toronto: Butterworths, 2001) at 685.
[5] J.S. Williams, *Law of Defamation in Canada* (Toronto: Butterworths, 1976) at 2.
[6] R.E. Brown, *The Law of Defamation in Canada* (Toronto: Thomson Canada, 1994) at 16.
[7] *Ibid.*, at 361
[8] J.S. Williams, *supra*, n. 5, at 60.
[9] J.G. Fleming, *The Law of Torts*, 9th ed. (Sydney: LBC Information Services, 1998), at 596.
[10] *Ibid.*
[11] *Supra*, n. 8, at 584.

The words used in a defamatory statement may themselves not be defamatory, but the imputation may be defamatory.[12] It is therefore obvious that many statements that could affect a person's reputation may be recorded in health records and regarded as defamatory. The statements could reflect on other patients, family, friends, associates, staff and even those who are unknown to the patient. The statements may originate with any of these sources as well.

It should also be noted that defamatory statements may arise from sources other than those recorded in the health records. Of particular note are minutes of staff, facility and board committees. The minutes may record defamatory comments or reports of such comments made by persons attending the committee meeting.

LIBEL AND SLANDER

Defamation under common law traditionally consisted of the two torts, or civil wrongs, of libel and slander. Libel is defamation in writing, whereas slander is spoken. To succeed in an action for libel, it was not necessary to prove injury. Injury had to be proven in a successful slander suit.[13] Most provinces have abolished this distinction by combining the two into an action for defamation in which injury need not be proven.[14]

APPLICATION TO HEALTH INFORMATION

It is apparent that statements in health information may be defamatory and are potentially the subject of legal action against any person making such statements. The fact that Canadian case law is sparse in such cases does not mean that an action in defamation could not occur. However, the defences available to those involved with health information reduce the opportunities for a successful action based on defamation.

---

[12] *Ibid.*

[13] J.S. Williams, *supra*, n. 5, at 54.

[14] See *e.g.*, *Defamation Act*, R.S.A. 2000, c. D-7; R.S.N.W.T. 1988, c. D-l; R.S.N.B. 1973, c. D-5; R.S.M. 1987, c. D20; R.S.N.S. 1989, c. 122; R.S.N. 1990, c. D-3; R.S.S. 1978, c. L-14; R.S.O. 1990, c. L.12; R.S.B.C. 1996, c. 263; R.S.P.E.I. 1988, c. D-5; R.S.Y. 1986, c. 41.

DEFENCE OF QUALIFIED PRIVILEGE

Even if a statement is made that may be considered defamatory, the defence of qualified privilege may apply.

The question is whether this privilege applies to defamatory statements arising in health information.[15] The occasion that is most likely to invoke the protection of qualified privilege is that of statements made in the performance of a duty. This duty may be either legal or moral. The test as to whether a statement is one of qualified privilege is taken from *Watt v. Longsdon*:

> Would the great mass of right-minded men in the position of the defendant have considered it their duty, under the circumstances, to make the communication?[16]

It can be argued that the person such as a physician or nurse recording the defamatory statement of the patient or a third party, or making an original defamatory statement is acting under a duty. This duty is to the patient. As discussed in Chapter 4 — Standards for Health Information, those making entries in the record have the duty to place whatever information is necessary in the record to carry out the treatment and care of the patient or client. It will always be a matter of judgment as to whether the defamatory statement was or was not made pursuant to this duty. In any legal action, the court will determine whether the placing of the statement in the health record was necessary for the patient or client's treatment and care.[17]

This issue was dealt with by the Ontario Court of Appeal in the 1975 case of *Foran v. Richman*.[18] It was alleged that an entry in a hospital record along with other documents was defamatory. The Court found that there was no serious contest as all the documents were written on occasions of qualified privilege.

Mr. Justice Arnup stated:

> In those circumstances the law is quite clear that the author of the allegedly defamatory material, where he has written under circumstances of qualified privilege, is presumed to have acted in good faith and in the honesty of belief of the truth of his statements, and further

---

15   This is a question of law for the judge. *Wade & Wells Co. v. Laing* (1957), 23 W.W.R. 106, 11 D.L.R. (2d) 276 (B.C.C.A.). The judge also decides how extensive the privilege is. *Adam v. Ward*, [1917] A.C. 309, at 328, [1916-17] All E.R. Rep. 157 (H.L.).

16   [1930] 1 K.B. 130, at 153, [1929] All E.R. Rep. 284 (C.A.).

17   A.M. Linden, *Canadian Tort Law*, 7th ed. (Toronto: Butterworths, 2001) at 714-718.

18   (1975), 10 O.R. (2d) 634, 64 D.L.R. (3d) 230 (C.A.), leave to appeal to S.C.C. refused 10 O.R. *loc. cit.*, D.L.R. *loc. cit.*

that the burden lies upon the plaintiff to rebut that presumption by affirmative proof of malice.[19]

Qualified privilege may be lost if the defendant were to record the statement for the purpose of maliciously harming someone. However, because the law would presume that any statement in the health record was there for the purpose of treatment and care, the person suing for defamation has the onus of proving that the purpose was malicious.[20]

The most important principle that must be noted is that the defence of a qualified privilege only extends to that part of the record which is made pursuant to the duty to the individual.[21] Any statement or part of a statement that is not relevant to treatment or care would not be protected and would be subject to an action for libel. This would be particularly true if information were included that is irrelevant to the care being provided.

When recording statements about patients, long term care residents, home care clients, staff or about third parties, great care must be taken to ensure that the reason for making the recording is to further the treatment and care of the patient. The protection of qualified privilege may also be lost if those to whom the information is published have no interest in receiving it.[22]

RECORD AMENDMENT AND CORRECTION

The risks associated with claims of defamation can be minimized by training staff to adhere to basic style requirements for recording information. A threshold consideration is "relevancy". Documentation should contain entries that are relevant and necessary for purposes of treatment. Orientation and in-service training should make clear what are and what are not considered acceptable entries in the record. Further, staff should have an opportunity to "practice" by utilizing case studies or participating in role-playing activities.

Records should be monitored for unacceptable entries through quality and risk management techniques. Conjecture, expansive speculation, and editorializing are "indicators" of risk-prone records.

Agency policies should include a process for record amendment and correction. Record amendment and correction procedures are particularly important where health care information is riddled with conjecture

---

[19] *Ibid.*, at 637 (O.R.).

[20] *Ibid.*

[21] *Adam v. Ward, supra,* n. 15, at 320, 321.

[22] *Pulp & Paper Workers of Canada v. International Brotherhood of Pulp, Sulphite & Paper Mill Workers,* [1973] 4 W.W.R. 160, 37 D.L.R. (3d) 687 (B.C.S.C.).

or unsubstantiated speculation. These procedures are equally important where individuals have access to their records or where individuals make entries themselves in the record. Challenges as to the accuracy of the record should be handled in accordance with established policy and procedure. This should include a method for recording an individual's stated objection where the caregiver refuses to modify the charted information.

Amendment and correction of health records is sometimes required by legislation.[23] This requirement may arise in access to information legislation, which has been enacted federally as well as in every province and territory in Canada. The requirement to correct, amend or include a statement of disagreement in the record also exists in jurisdictions that have health information legislation.[24] These issues are discussed in more detail in Chapter 7 — Access to Health Information.

The key to avoiding defamatory information in the patient's records is "relevancy". The information must be relevant to the treatment and care of the patient and should not be put in the record unless it is relevant to the duties of those who will read it. Personal comments which are not relevant to care must be avoided. Health information must not be a repository for the personal frustrations or the philosophies of caregivers. Even veiled comments and innuendoes must be avoided.[25]

---

[23] See *e.g.*, *Mental Health Act*, R.S.M. 1987, c. M110, s. 26.9(9), dealing with the right of correction. See also, "Principles for Proposed Legislation on Health Care Information Access and Privacy" (Canadian Institute of Law and Medicine Conference, 6 December 1991) in which a process for handling corrections is discussed.

[24] See *e.g.*, *The Personal Health Information Act*, S.M. 1997, c. 51 (C.C.S.M., c. P33.5), s. 12; *Health Information Act*, R.S.A. 2000, c. H-5, ss. 13 and 14.

[25] *Supra*, n. 3, at 691 and 722.

15

Employee Health Information

OVERVIEW

The growth in occupational health and safety requirements and new access and privacy legislation has spawned considerable interest in employee health information. The topic is unfamiliar territory for medicolegal, ethical and quality management issues. Employee health information exists in widely divergent settings and involves virtually all employers. This information is of interest not only to employers and employees, but also to a multitude of third parties such as insurance companies and financial institutions.

Employee health involves a triangle of three parties, rather than the two parties involved in the usual doctor-patient relationship. This arrangement gives rise to unique questions, such as whether a doctor-patient relationship exists between the occupational health physician and the employee or alternatively between the physician and the employer.

Does the physician have a duty to provide a detailed medical report or just an opinion about fitness for employment to the employer? What information is the employee entitled to request? This chapter will highlight some key issues to consider for developing cogent practices for employee health information.

WHAT IS EMPLOYEE HEALTH INFORMATION?

Employers and health care agencies may have their own definition of what constitutes employee health information. Descriptions of employee health information may be found in policies and procedures located in human resources, employee handbooks, collective agreements and in contracts of employment.

There can be confusion about the information that should be kept in human resources and infection control areas as opposed to employee health files. For example, fitness for employment is assessed when hiring new staff. Health status may relate to performance issues. Employers may conduct employee drug or infectious disease testing. If there is ambiguity about what will be included in an employee health file, the uncertainty should be clarified.

Health information legislation has defined health information in some provinces.[1] For example, the *Health Information Act*[2] in Alberta includes three kinds of information in the definition of health information — diagnostic, treatment and care information; registration information; and health services provider information. The definition of "health services provider information" is broad and includes information about continued competencies, restrictions on practice, decisions of professional disciplinary bodies, business arrangements and employment status. Health sector employers such as regional health authorities, provincial boards and health providers such as physicians are bound by this legislation.

Other public sector employers are bound by freedom of information and protection of privacy (FOIP) legislation[3] that defines "personal information" as including health information. Private sector employers may be bound by the federal *Personal Information Protection and Electronic Documents Act (PIPEDA)*,[4] which also contains a detailed definition of "personal health information".

Some employers keep detailed information while other employers keep little information in employee health files. Unless there is legislation that defines employee health information, this is pretty much what each employer says it is. However, clarity and transparency is important and there should be no surprises about the information that an employer will record in an employee health file.

---

[1]   The *Personal Health Information Act*, S.M. 1997, c. 51; *Health Information Protection Act*, S.S. 1999, c. H-0.021 (Note — enacted but not yet proclaimed); *Ontario Draft Privacy of Personal Information Act, 2002*, A Draft for Consultation; *Health Information Act*, R.S.A. 2000, c. H-5.

[2]   *Health Information Act, supra,* n. 1, s. 1(1).

[3]   *Freedom of Information and Protection of Privacy Act*, R.S.B.C. 1996, c. 165; *Freedom of Information and Protection of Privacy Act*, R.S.A. 2000, c. F-18.5; *Protection of Personal Information Act*, S.N.B. 2001, c. P-19.1, proclaimed April 2001; *Freedom of Information Act*, R.S.N. 1990, c. F-25; *Privacy Act*, R.S.N. 1990, c. P-22; *Access to Information and Protection of Privacy Act (Nunavut)*, S.N.W.T. 1994, c. 20 (Nunavut enacted under s. 76.05 of *Nunavut Act*); *Access to Information and Protection of Privacy Act*, S.N.W.T. 1994, c. 20; *Freedom of Information and Protection of Privacy Act*, S.N.S. 1993, c. 5; *Freedom of Information and Protection of Privacy Act*, R.S.O. 1990, c. F.31; *Municipal Freedom of Information and Protection of Privacy Act*, R.S.O. 1990, c. M.56; *Act Respecting Access to Documents held by Public Bodies and the Protection of Personal Information*, R.S.Q. 1993, c. A-2.1, enacted on June 22, 1982; *Freedom of Information and Protection of Privacy Act*, S.S. 1990-91, c. F-22.01; *Local Authority Freedom of Information and Protection of Privacy Act*, S.S. 1990-91, c. L-27.1; *Access to Information and Protection of Privacy Act*, S.Y. 1995, c. 1; *Freedom of Information and Protection of Privacy Act, (No. 2)*, S.P.E.I. 2001, c. 37 (Bill 47), Royal Assent May 15, 2001, not yet proclaimed.

[4]   *Personal Information Protection and Electronic Documents Act*, S.C. 2000, c. 5, first part proclaimed in force in January 2001.

INTERVIEWS AND REFERENCE CHECKS

Employers often conduct initial and exit interviews. Pre-employment interviews are conducted to ascertain whether the employee is suitable for the position. Occupational health requirements should be discussed at this time. The exit interview is a good opportunity to remind employees of their health status. This is particularly important for healthcare workers who are due for additional hepatitis vaccine, flu shots, blood tests to determine the need for hepatitis vaccine boosters, or other vaccinations. The employer should make a note that the employee has been "reminded" of these responsibilities.

Reference checks focus upon the ability and suitability of an individual to perform a particular job. Overall performance, attendance at work and other factors that involve health information may be important concerns for a new employer. Reference information is particularly sensitive and may be extremely harmful to an individual.

Due to liability concerns, some employers will only provide minimal information such as dates of employment. References are particularly difficult when performance concerns exist. However, inadequate reference information may mean that an individual with a known performance problem is just passed along to a new employer. References involving health information should ideally be provided on the basis of consent and always in strict accordance with employer policy.

COLLECTION, USE AND DISCLOSURE

Many employers conduct "fitness for employment" and annual physical examinations. Employers in high risk businesses routinely conduct on-going employee drug testing for safety reasons. Occupational health testing may be required when performance issues arise. Prospective employees should be advised of these practices, so the type of information in employee health records is not a surprise to workers.

It is important that employers, employees and physicians have a clear understanding of the health information that can be used and disclosed for employment purposes. In the Ontario case of *Miron v. Pohran*,[5] an employee sued a physician when he warned her employer following an annual employment physical examination and she lost her job. The physician considered health information that he obtained when he saw the employee as a patient in the emergency department previously. The employee was unsuccessful as she had signed a written consent that did not restrict the information that could be used.

---

[5]   (1981), 8 A.C.W.S. (2d) 509 (Ont. Co. Ct.).

Health sector enactments establish requirements for employee health information.[6] Some enactments require health care agencies to record test results at certain time frames, such as pre-employment, near the beginning of employment or at the end of employment. Health care agencies may be required to record the results of specific tests such as chest x-rays or tuberculin tests.[7]

Some jurisdictions require test results on an ongoing basis, for example care facilities in B.C. must have annual chest x-ray reports for employees.[8] Some jurisdictions have very detailed requirements, such as the North West Territories, which requires comprehensive pre-employment examinations, annual exams, chest x-rays, tuberculin tests, and urinalysis, blood and other tests as prescribed, and proof of immunization.[9]

Specific legal requirements exist for particular industries. For example, commercial pilots must undergo annual physicals and physicians must report the results as specified.[10] Occupational health legislation requires test results to be recorded in industries that involve exposure to asbestos, silica, coal dust and noise.[11]

Health information is required to manage and compensate employees involved in workplace injuries. Employees may be referred to internal or external employee assistance programs. Insurers and adjudicators need to make determinations about whether workers were injured at work or had pre-existing problems. Medical histories and genetic predisposition to illness and injury is extremely sensitive health information.

Paramedics may be exposed to body fluids, nurses may sustain needlesticks, surgeons may be cut with scalpel blades and central service workers may be cut with sharp instruments. Employees may undergo testing or treatment for occupational exposure to infectious diseases such as HIV or Hepatitis B or C. There are legitimate concerns about blood testing the exposed employee.

Some jurisdictions have taken steps toward mandatory blood testing for individuals who may have infected emergency workers.[12] There are implications for even being tested for an infectious disease such as HIV. For example, a standard question when applying for insurance is

---

[6]   *Care Facilities Regulations*, B.C. Reg. 337/88, s. 30; *Hospital Management Regulations*, P.E.I. Reg. EC 574/76, s. 60; *Hospital Standards Act*, R.S.S. 1978, c. H-10, s. 92; Sask. Reg. 132/81, s. 5; Ont. — *Private Hospitals Act Regulation*, R.R.O. 1990, Reg. 937, ss. 25-31; *Hospital Act Regulation*, N.B. Reg. 92-84, ss. 56-57; and *Hospital Standards Regulation*, R.R.N.W.T. 1990, c. T-6, s. 62.

[7]   *Ibid*.

[8]   *Care Facilities Regulation*, *supra*, n. 6.

[9]   *Hospital Standards Regulation*, R.R.N.W.T. 1990, c. T-6, s. 62.

[10] *Aeronautics Act*, R.S.C. 1985, c. A-2.

[11] See *e.g.*, *Chemical Hazards Regulation*, Alta. Reg. 393/88, s. 41-44.

[12] *Blood Samples Act*, Bill C-217, read for the second time and referred to committee on May 15, 2001. It now appears that this proposed Act will not be enacted.

whether a person has been tested for specific infectious diseases such as HIV.

Treatment received in the context of employee health programs may relate to sensitive health issues such as drug or addiction counselling or mental health problems. Much depends on whether such programs are outsourced. If the employer is operating the program, all the health information may be on the employee health record. It is important to settle the issue of what will be recorded on the employee record as early as possible in the process. This information may affect employee decisions such as whether to accept services offered by an employee or to obtain care privately.

Researchers may wish to abstract data from employee health records for purposes of scientific investigation. If this is the case, do researchers abstract data themselves, or is this done for them by the employer? Are researchers permitted to use identifiable information so they can data-match or link records with specific individuals? Does this mean that a present or former employee can be contacted for more in-depth analysis as part of a research protocol?

Human rights legislation prohibits discrimination on the basis of physical and mental disability.[13] Similarly, the *Canadian Charter of Rights and Freedoms* guarantees all Canadians the right to be treated equally and not discriminated against on the basis of factors such as age, mental and physical disability.[14] Employers are required to treat employees fairly based upon legitimate health requirements to perform the work.

Depending upon the employer, detailed rules for the collection, use and disclosure of personal information including health information may apply. The most likely types of legislation include health information legislation, FOIP legislation and *PIPEDA*. Disclosure of health information is discussed in more detail in Chapter 8 — Confidentiality, Privacy and Disclosure to Third Parties. These types of provisions typically require either consent or statutory exemptions for collection, use and disclosure of health information.

The best approach is to review legislative and other requirements and then clearly delineate a consistent approach in policy and procedure. Procedures should address issues of particular concern such as requests from employers, benefit plans, insurers, workers' compensation claims, researchers, lawyers and police.

---

[13] See *e.g.*, *Human Rights, Citizenship and Multiculturalism Act*, R.S.A. 2000, c. H-14.

[14] *Canadian Charter of Rights and Freedoms*, Part I of the *Constitution Act, 1982*, Schedule B to the *Canada Act 1982* (U.K.) 1982, c. 11, s. 15.

ACCESS BY EMPLOYEES

Employees may request access to their own health information. The handling of an access request from an employee for their own information varies from employer to employer and varies with the circumstances of the request. Ideally, employers should review legislative and other requirements and address this situation clearly in policies and procedures so that the employer as well as the employees understand the process.

Similar to the new rules for disclosure, legislation has created new legal rights of access for individuals seeking their own health information. Similarly, legislation such as freedom of information and protection of privacy (FOIP) legislation and *PIPEDA* establishes a right of access for individuals to their own personal information.

Jurisdictions with health information legislation have detailed rules for individuals to access their own health information. There are exceptions to access such as harm to the individual or threat to the safety of others or the public. Individuals can request correction or amendment to their health record. Individuals may make an access request to find out to whom their health information has been disclosed. Access by individuals to their own health information is discussed in more detail in Chapter 7 — Access to Health Information.

RETENTION, STORAGE AND DISPOSAL

How long should health records be maintained after an employee leaves? Does the information have to be stored or destroyed in a particular manner? These are common questions posed to health records experts. There are no simple answers to these questions. Much depends on applicable legislative and regulatory requirements, employer policies, and the purposes for which the information is maintained.

As noted in Chapter 5 — Retention, Storage and Disposal, employers should take into account the various uses for the health information. If an employer is conducting longitudinal studies of the effect of protective clothing, headgear or earplugs, the records may be kept for a considerable length of time. If the employer is embroiled in what promises to be protracted wrongful dismissal litigation over health-related matters, the retention period may be longer than in the ordinary course of record keeping for that business.

The best approach is to look at the ways in which the health information is used and to establish a basic retention period. Exceptions can be built in for exceptional situations. Once in place, the employer can determine the most cost-effective yet legally acceptable method for storing the information. Microfilming, CD ROM copies, or hard copy text storage might be considered. Experts in the field of health information management can advise on what is most appropriate for the specific circumstances.

When the time comes to dispose of the information, experts should again be consulted for advice on destroying the files. A cautious approach is advisable, such as contacting senior management or Human Resources for final clearance before destroying the information. This additional step is warranted, particularly in larger companies or agencies where one group may be unaware of litigation or other needs for prolonged retention of health information.

Lawsuits in which prolonged exposure to chemicals, airborne particulate, and other occupational exposure continue to demonstrate the importance of good employee health record keeping. The absence of salient information can make it very difficult to defend against occupationally linked claims. Hence, the precaution of a clear process and final clearance before destroying health information is important.

PRACTICAL CONSIDERATIONS

1. *Review Applicable Legislation, Guidelines and Agreements* — Employers should consider seeking legal advice to review and interpret relevant legislation, agreements and requirements for handling employee health information.

2. *Describe Employee Health Information* — Employers should create and provide employees with a clear description of employee health information and the type of information that will be kept on employee health files.

3. *Interviews and References* — Employers should establish and implement clear policies and procedures for conducting initial and exit interviews and reference checks.

4. *Collection, Use and Disclosure* — Employers should establish and implement clear policies and procedures that are consistent with legal and other requirements for the collection, use and disclosure of employee health information.

5. *Access by Employees* — Employers should establish and implement clear policies and procedures that are consistent with legal requirements for the access, amendment and correction of employee health information.

6. *Retention, Storage and Disposal* — Employers should establish and implement clear policies and procedures that are consistent with legal requirements for the retention, storage and disposal of employee health information.

Taking these preventive measures can assist employers and health care agencies in avoiding many difficulties involving employee health information.

16

Human Research and Health Information

ISSUES

Health information forms the basis of the information required to conduct human health research projects. Accurate observations and findings must be recorded for researchers to determine the effectiveness of new drugs, psychological or behavioural interventions, and novel medical or surgical procedures. Documentation is an important consideration where research is conducted in conjunction with established treatment to distinguish ongoing care from experimental therapy. The failure to keep accurate information can jeopardize research findings. Incomplete notations could threaten an individual's well-being.

Research projects may utilize health information without contacting the subject of the information. Research may involve retrospective, concurrent or prospective epidemiological studies. Health conditions such as cross-infection, cancer morbidity, heart disease, mental illness and drug abuse may be studied. Many researchers find it difficult to understand how a "record search" or statistical research study constitutes human research. Research raises particular concerns for privacy where the research is a secondary use or disclosure of health information that was not contemplated by the individual.

The health data along with individual identifiers may provide enough information to link the findings to specific persons. Where this is the case and the data contains sensitive information, any unauthorized disclosure could prove highly damaging. The disclosure may adversely affect a person's family, livelihood, and status in the community. Because of the potential danger from unauthorized disclosure, many types of record searches are considered research and require steps such as consent and research committee approval.

It may be difficult to determine whether an activity is internal quality management, evaluation and monitoring or alternatively is human research. Where the activity is just for internal information such as patient satisfaction surveys or evaluation of service changes, this is more likely to be quality management. Alternatively, where the intention is external publication and sharing of new knowledge the activity is more likely to be research. This determination needs to be made at the beginning of a project as end results such as external publication may be thwarted if research review requirements are not met.

LEGISLATION

Human research involving health information is a matter much discussed in Canadian legislation and regulations.[1] The legislation relating to access and confidentiality of health information has been discussed in more detail in earlier chapters (Chapter 7 — Access to Health Information and Chapter 8 — Confidentiality, Privacy and Disclosure to Third Parties).

Some enactments are general and apply to all types of personal information, including health information. Freedom of information legislation applies to personal information in the public sector and now exists federally, provincially and in the territories. For example, the *Freedom of Information and Protection of Privacy Act*[2] in British Columbia says:

> 35. A public body may disclose personal information for a research purpose, including statistical research, only if
>   (a) the research purpose cannot reasonably be accomplished unless that information is provided in individually identifiable form or the research purpose has been approved by the commissioner,
>   (b) any record linkage is not harmful to the individuals that information is about and the benefits to be derived from the record linkage are clearly in the public interest,
>   (c) the head of the public body concerned has approved conditions relating to the following:
>   (i)   security and confidentiality;
>   (ii)   the removal or destruction of individual identifiers at the earliest reasonable time;
>   (iii) the prohibition of any subsequent use or disclosure of that information in individually identifiable form without the express authorization of that public body, and
>   (d) the person to whom that information is disclosed has signed an agreement to comply with the approved conditions, this Act and any of the public body's policies and procedures relating to the confidentiality of personal information.[3]

---

[1] Canadian Institutes of Health Research, *A Compendium of Canadian Legislation Respecting the Protection of Personal Information in Health Research*, April 2000; Canadian Institutes of Health Research, *Selected International Legal Norms on the Protection of Personal Information in Health Research*, December 2001.

[2] *Freedom of Information and Protection of Privacy Act*, R.S.B.C. 1996, c. 165.

[3] *Ibid.*, s. 35.

Private sector legislation applies to personal information and now exists federally and in Quebec, and is being considered in other jurisdictions. The *Personal Information Protection and Electronic Documents Act* *(PIPEDA)*[4] allows an organization to use and disclose personal information without consent for "statistical or scholarly study or research purposes" where: purposes cannot be achieved without disclosing the information, confidentiality is ensured, it is impractical to obtain consent and the organization informs the Commissioner of the disclosure.[5] In Quebec information may be used or disclosed without consent for "study, research or statistical purposes" when the commissioner grants authorization and where the information is essential for research and confidentiality is ensured.[6]

Some enactments specifically deal with health information for research purposes. Health information legislation has been recently enacted in Manitoba, Saskatchewan (not yet proclaimed) and Alberta, and a draft for discussion has been released in Ontario.[7] This type of legislation contains detailed provisions relating to health research. For example, the Manitoba legislation says:

> 24(1) A trustee may disclose personal health information to a person conducting a health research project only if the project has been approved under this section.
>
>   (2) An approval may be given by
>   (a)   the health information privacy committee established under section 59, if the personal health information is maintained by the government or a government agency; and
>   (b)   an institutional research review committee, if the personal health information is maintained by a trustee other than the government or a government agency.
>   (3) An approval may be given under this section only if the health information privacy committee, as the case may be, has determined that
>   (a)   the research is of sufficient importance to outweigh the intrusion into privacy that would result from the disclosure of personal health information;

---

[4]   *Personal Information Protection and Electronic Documents Act*, S.C. 2000, c. 5, assented to April 2000, first part proclaimed in force in January 2001.

[5]   *Ibid.*, s. 7(2) and(3).

[6]   An *Act Respecting the Protection of Personal Information in the Private Sector*, R.S.Q. c. P-39.1, ss. 18(5), 21.

[7]   *The Personal Health Information Act*, S.M. 1997, c. P-33.5, proclaimed in 1997; *The Health Information Protection Act*, S.S. 1999, c. H-0.021, Royal Assent in 1999, but not yet proclaimed; *Health Information Act*, R.S.A. 2000, c. H-5, proclaimed in April 2001; *Draft Privacy of Personal Information Act, 2002*, Ontario, released for discussion in January 2002.

(b)   the research purpose cannot reasonably be accomplished unless the personal health information is provided in a form that identifies or may identify individuals;

(c)   it is unreasonable or impractical for the person proposing the research to obtain consent from the individuals the personal health information is about; and

(d)   the research project contains

(i)   reasonable safeguards to protect the confidentiality and security of the personal health information, and

(ii) procedures to destroy the information or remove all identifying information at the earliest opportunity consistent with the purposes of the project.

(4) An approval under this section is conditional on the person proposing the research project entering into an agreement with the trustee, in accordance with the trustee, in accordance with the regulation, in which the person agrees

(a)   not to publish the personal health information requested in a form that could reasonably be expected to identify the individuals concerned;

(b)   to use the personal health information requested solely for the purposes of the approved research project; and

(c)   to ensure that the research project complies with the safeguards and procedures described in clause (3)(d).

(5) If a research project will require direct contact with individuals, a trustee shall not disclose personal health information about those individuals under this section without first obtaining their consent. However, the trustee need not obtain their consent if the information consists only of the individual's names and addresses.[8]

The Saskatchewan legislation requires approval by a research ethics committee and various other criteria to be met before health information can be used or disclosed for research purposes without consent, such as arrangements for returning or destroying the health information.[9]

Similarly, the Alberta legislation requires approval by an ethics committee that must consider specific areas such as whether the public interest in the research outweighs the privacy of the individuals, adequacy of privacy safeguards and whether consent is required.[10] A copy of the ethics committee approval must be provided to the Commissioner and a custodian must have an agreement with prescribed terms with a researcher before health information can be disclosed.[11] The agreement must contain a provision that the custodian may inspect the researcher's

---

[8]   *Ibid.*, s. 24.

[9]   *The Health Information Protection Act, supra*, n. 7, s. 29.

[10] *Health Information Act, supra*, n. 7, ss. 48-56.

[11] *Ibid.*, ss. 50, 54.

premises to ensure compliance with the agreement and the custodian may apply for a court order to conduct an inspection if this is refused.[12]

Enactments that govern research in the health sector have existed for a long time. These types of provisions usually address a specific area of health service. For example, the *Public Health Act*[13] in New Brunswick allows public health information to be disclosed for purposes of "bona fide research or medical review" if the anonymity of the individual is protected.[14]

The *Hospitals Act*[15] in Newfoundland and Labrador allows information from hospital records to be disclosed for purposes of "health or medical research" where the research is in the public interest, the information will not be disclosed in a way that is detrimental to the patient or a health provider.[16] In Ontario the *Cancer Act*[17] allows information to be disclosed for compiling statistics or carrying out "medical or epidemiological research".[18] In Manitoba, health information from a psychiatric facility[19] and regarding organ donation[20] may be disclosed for research with prescribed precautions.

The Law Commission of Canada commissioned an extensive study of the governance of health research,[21] which indicated that the complexity of Canadian governance arrangements creates significant ethical challenges. The study found that health research was characterized by "ethical tunnel vision" with a focus away from broad ethical values and toward bureaucratic tasks such as processing proposals and consent forms by research ethics boards (REBs) and with research subjects having little involvement in the governance of research.[22]

---

[12] *Ibid.*, s. 56.

[13] R.S.N.B. c. P-22.4.

[14] *Ibid.*, s. 66(2)(g); also see for example, *The Public Health Act*, R.S.S. 1994, c. P-37.1, s. 65(2)(d)(ii); *Public Health Act*, R.S.N.B., c. P-22.4, s. 66(2)(g); *Public Health Act*, R.S.A. 2000, c. P-37, s. 53(2).

[15] R.S.N.L. 1990, c. H-9.

[16] *Ibid.*, s. 35(4); also see for example, Hospital Management regulation under *Public Hospitals Act*, R.R.O. 1990, Reg. 965, s. 22(6)(f); *An Act Respecting Health Services and Social Services*, R.S.Q., c. S-4.2, s. 19; *Hospitals Act*, R.S.N.S. 1989, c. 208, s. 71(6); *Health Act*, R.S.N.B., c. H-2, s. 33(2); *The Health Act*, R.S.N.S. 1989, c. 195, s. 126(2).

[17] *The Cancer Act*, R.S.O. 1990, c. C.1.

[18] *Ibid.*, s. 7(1); also see for example, *Health Act*, R.S.B.C. 1996, c. 179, s. 9; *Cancer Programs Act*, R.S.A.. 2000, c. C-2, Part 2.

[19] *The Mental Health Act*, R.S.M. 1987, c. M-110, s. 26.9(2)(g).

[20] *The Human Tissue Gift Act*, S.M. 1987-88, c. 39 (C.C.S.M. c. H180) s. 13.

[21] Law Commission of Canada, *The Governance of Health Research Involving Human Subjects (HRIHS)*, (Ottawa: Law Commission of Canada, 2000).

[22] *Ibid.*, at v-xiv, 346-349.

In 1989 the Law Reform Commission of Canada made recommendations in a Working Paper[23] that although not incorporated into *the Criminal Code* of Canada as recommended, provided substantive principles that are still being incorporated into research and legal provisions. Some health care agencies have developed their specific approach to research from ethical guidelines such as the Helsinki Declaration that has been adopted by the World Medical Association several years ago.[24]

Legislative requirements have been influenced by the common law. For example, as a result of the *Halushka v. University of Saskatchewan* case,[25] a high standard of informed consent is required for participation in research. In the *Halushka* case, a medical student participated in research that involved a cardiac catheterization where a catheter is put into the heart. The student was only told that the research would involve a general anaesthetic and a catheter. He was not told that the product was new and would be put into the heart. During the procedure, the student had a heart attack that caused permanent injury. The University was held liable for the failure to obtain informed consent.

Research requirements are also influenced by incidents that occur in research projects. For example controversy arose when a researcher, Dr. Nancy Olivieri, disclosed her concerns about a drug she was testing for the manufacturer Apotex Inc. at the Hospital for Sick Children in Toronto.[26] The researcher had signed a contract with the drug manufacturer and had been forbidden to disclose the potential risks she had identified in the research drug trial either to the subjects or the scientific community.

Dr. Olivieri went public in May of 1996. Apotex threatened litigation and claimed that the researcher was in breach of a confidentiality agreement. The Canadian Association of University Teachers compiled a comprehensive report and identified serious failings in the safeguards for research subjects. The hospital and university have since revised research processes and contracts.

Aside from legal provisions there are authoritative Canadian guidelines for human research. Two of the most important guidelines are prepared by the Tri-Council and the Canadian Institutes of Health Research (CIHR).

---

[23] Law Reform Commission of Canada, *Biomedical Experimentation Involving Human Subjects*, Working Paper 61, Ottawa, 1989, at 61-63.

[24] World Medical Association Declaration of Helsinki, *Ethical Principles for Medical Research Involving Human Subjects*, first adopted by the World Medical Association 1964, amended for the fifth time in October of 2000 at the 52nd WMA General Assembly in Edinburgh, Scotland.

[25] (1965), 53 D.L.R. (2d) 436 (Sask. C.A.).

[26] "Report Backs Whistle-Blower", *Edmonton Journal* (27 October 2001) A16.

TRI-COUNCIL POLICY STATEMENT

The Tri-Council was composed of three Councils: the Medical Research Council of Canada (MRC), the Natural Sciences and Engineering Research Council of Canada (NSERC) and the Social Sciences and Humanities Research Council of Canada (SSHRC), all of whom were created by Acts of Parliament.[27] The *Tri-Council Policy Statement: Ethical Conduct for Research Involving Humans* of 1998[28] has replaced earlier guidelines published by the MRC[29] and the SSHRC.[30]

The Tri-Council Policy Statement provides ethical standards for research. This Statement does not have the same legal effect as statutes or regulations. Nonetheless, the Statement carries significant weight as the three Councils are major funding sources for human research in Canada. The Councils will not provide or continue funding unless individuals or facilities certify compliance with this policy. Therefore most facilities and researchers follow the requirements.

The Tri-Council Policy Statement provides detailed guidelines on the ethics review process that each research protocol must undergo before being approved. Detailed guidelines are provided for establishing Review Ethics Boards (REBs), weighing the risks and benefits, and review procedures including record keeping. Matters such as clinical trials, consent, privacy and confidentiality and conflict of interest are addressed. Research involving aboriginal people, genetic research, human gametes, embryos, fetuses and human tissue is discussed at length.[31]

CANADIAN INSTITUTES OF HEALTH RESEARCH

The CIHR was established by an Act of Parliament[32] to replace the MRC. The CIHR has continued the legislative mandate to approve research funding and develop policies but the mandate has been expanded to areas

---

[27] *Medical Research Council Act*, R.S.C. 1985, c. M-4; *Natural Science and Engineering Research Council Act*, R.S.C. 1985, c. N-21; *Social Sciences and Humanities Research Council Act*, R.S.C. 1985, c. S-12.

[28] Medical Research Council of Canada, Natural Sciences and Engineering Research Council of Canada, Social Sciences and Humanities Research Council of Canada, *Tri-Council Policy Statement: Ethical Conduct for Research Involving Humans*, (Ottawa: Public Works and Government Services Canada, 1998), Article 1.11 Section 1 and Article 1.2 B1 Section 1 amended as of March 2002.

[29] Medical Research Council of Canada, *Guidelines on Research Involving Human Subjects*, (Ottawa: Minister of Supply and Services, 1987).

[30] Social Sciences and Humanities Research Council of Canada, *Ethics Guidelines for Research Involving Human Subjects*, Ottawa, 1977.

[31] *Tri-Council Policy Statement: Ethical Conduct for Research Involving Humans*, *supra*, n. 28.

[32] *Canadian Institutes of Health Research Act*, S.C. 2000, c. 6.

such as establishing a peer review process for research proposals.[33] The CIHR has substantial additional ancillary powers that include the authority to enter into partnerships and to form corporate entities to carry out its mandate.[34]

The CIHR is taking a lead role in the health research and policy area. Recent CIHR publications demonstrate partnerships with other federal organizations such as the Canadian Institute of Health Information (CIHI),[35] and analysis of future developments such as the potential impact of *PIPEDA* on health research in Canada.[36] The Panel on Research Ethics as well as a Secretariat on Research Ethics is being formed by the three funding agencies of CIHR, SSHRC and NSERC, to provide a new governance structure to support the continued development of the Tri-Council Policy Statement.[37] The CIHR has recently issued guidelines on the controversial issue of stem cell research,[38] which will apply to all CIHR funded research.

CONFIDENTIALITY AND PRIVACY

The confidentiality and privacy of health information when conducting human research is discussed in the Tri-Council Policy Statement, particularly for the secondary use of data and data linkage.[39] Health information used for research purposes may be stored in individual files such as patient charts or in composite form such as in registries or in data banks.

---

[33] *Ibid.*, s. 14.

[34] *Ibid.*, s. 26.

[35] *Personal Information Protection and Electronic Documents Act: Questions and Answers for Health Researchers*, (Ottawa: CIHR and CIHI, 2001).

[36] *Background Legal Research and Analysis in Support of CIHR's Recommendations with Respect to the Protection of Personal Information and Electronic Documents* (Ottawa: CIHR, 2001), *Recommendations for the Interpretation and Application of the Protection of Personal Information and Electronic Documents Act in Health Research Context*, (Ottawa: CIHR, 2001); *Case Studies Involving Secondary Use of Personal Information in Health Research* (Ottawa: CIHR, 2001), *Draft Recommendations for the Interpretation and Application of the Protection of Personal Information and Electronic Documents Act in Health Research*, Discussion Document (Ottawa: CIHR, 2001).

[37] *Governance Structure for the Tri-Council Policy Statement: Ethical Conduct for Research Involving Humans*, Terms of Reference (2001-2006); Call for Nominations for Panel Members, Panel on Research Ethics, CIHR, NSERC and SSHRC.

[38] *CIHR Guidelines on Human Pluripotent Stem Cell Research*, (Ottawa: CIHR, Effective March 4, 2002).

[39] *Tri-Council Policy Statement: Ethical Conduct for Research Involving Humans*, *supra*, n. 28, Section 3, Privacy and Confidentiality, at 3.1-3.6.

Epidemiological studies based on retrospective or prospective data sometimes require individual follow-up, a factor that poses a particularly difficult problem. Most individuals do not realize that their health record is not a confidential volume of information. They do not appreciate that it is open to students, public health and hospital officials, and in some cases, provincial regulatory bodies. In each of these instances, individuals may accept these intrusions as part of the health care system. The same may not be true, however, for use or disclosure for research purposes.

Striking a balance between subject anonymity and conducting research may prove a difficult task. Sometimes the goal of anonymity can be achieved by coding health information, restricting the number of people who see the records, or by removing all individual identifiers. However, sometimes the research protocol requires contact or follow-up of individuals, necessitating the use of identifiers.

Maintaining confidentiality in the publication of health information may be easier to achieve than in the actual collection of data. The author of a paper on a research project can refer to subjects in global terms, using few specifics that can link a particular individual to research findings. If individual identification is necessary, however, it is incumbent upon the researcher to get signed authorization to publish such personal data. The failure to obtain consent could lead to allegations of breach of confidentiality and privacy.

CONSENT

The importance and difficulties of obtaining consent in human research is evident in the Tri-Council Policy Statement discussion of difficulties such as ensuring voluntariness, informed consent, determining capacity and handling emergency situations.[40] It would be impractical if not impossible to contact every individual for permission to review their health information as part of a research project. Some provincial regulations recognize this and specifically provide for research without the individual's permission.[41]

Some health agencies address the issue at the outset of care, securing an authorization for researchers to either review health information in the course of approved studies or contact the individual as part of an

---

[40] *Tri-Council Policy Statement: Ethical Conduct for Research Involving Humans, supra,* n. 28, Section 2, Free and Informed Consent, at 2.1-2.12.

[41] See *e.g.*, Canadian Institutes of Health Research, *A Compendium of Canadian Legislation Respecting the Protection of Personal Information in Health Research, supra,* n. 1, and *supra,* n. 7.

approved research project. The individual has the right to refuse to agree to participate in research or disclose health information for research purposes. A refusal should be clearly noted in the health record.

Caution should be exercised in the way in which follow-up of an individual is initiated. Chronically ill individuals may not wish to take part in research. Follow-up studies involving end-stage cardiac, renal or cancer patients can be particularly burdensome. The individual's disease may be too far advanced to take part or the individual may have died. A telephone call made to an extremely ill or deceased individual's home may be extremely upsetting for a distraught relative.

Whenever possible, researchers should try to ascertain the potential subject's health status before making any contact. Vital statistics registries and local newspapers may be consulted as well as the individual's attending physician. The family physician would usually know whether the individual's health status would enable participation in a follow-up study.

Sometimes the individual is merely an index subject through whom relatives may be contacted to conduct investigations of genetic or familial links to disease. The medical advisor or the custodian or trustee of the health information may be the intermediary with the subject or the family. This is an issue that the investigator should address in the proposal before the ethics review committee. This may be an important additional step if there is an ethical duty to warn relatives, for example of genetically based disorders.

Some issues arise with using the custodian, trustee or the family member's medical advisor to contact the index subject or the potential subject. How would the custodian obtain the contact information in the first place? Many clinicians may be reluctant to take on this role. The trend is toward the custodian making initial and additional contact for permission for the researcher to contact the research subject or relative. This could be followed up with a telephone call or personal interview with the researcher to determine if each individual is willing to participate.

The advantage of this system of contact is that it maintains confidentiality and reduces the possibility of undue pressure from the researcher. However, the disadvantage is that no further contact with the index subject or the family may occur depending upon the outcome of the communication. The success of any contact will depend in large measure upon the relationship established between the researcher and the index subject and between the researcher and the custodian as well as the approach used by the custodian with potential research participants.

Maintaining confidentiality of health information in human research requires diligence on the part of all concerned. The research director is ultimately responsible for health information in the research records.

However, the health care agency or custodian/trustee still has its own duty regarding such information. It is important to continually educate personnel regarding duties and liabilities for unauthorized disclosure of health information. The educational process can be carried out as part of an in-service training program as well as orientation courses for newcomers to any research project.

Requiring researchers to enter into agreements and sign "confidentiality pledges" is important. If a staff researcher violates the agreement or the pledge, this may be grounds for dismissal. If a research subject is harmed as the result of an unauthorized disclosure, the subject may sue the research director as well as the researcher. The signed agreement and the confidentiality pledge indicates that the researcher had an obligation to maintain confidentiality and was aware of this duty.

If a custodian or a research director was sued successfully for a breach of confidentiality as the result of the actions of a researcher employee, a signed agreement and confidentiality pledge could be used in any subsequent action for indemnification. It would demonstrate that the employee was cognizant of the duty of confidentiality of health information. This would not, however, excuse the research director or custodian from vicarious liability as an employer.

Confidentiality pledges should be tailored to meet the needs of individual projects and institutions. However, there is basic information that the forms should include, such as the following:

- a description of the project;
- the nature of the sensitive information;
- the way in which an unauthorized disclosure could be damaging;
- the employee's duties in maintaining confidentiality; and
- the consequences of making an unauthorized disclosure of health information.

A sample of a confidentiality pledge may be found in the Appendix.

Strict security is required. Security measures such as limited access and periodic changes of passwords and entry codes are important considerations. Where possible, health information should be coded to limit the possibility of breaches of privacy. The number of individuals with access code designations should be kept to a minimum. All security measures should be reviewed at least annually to determine if more effective measures are needed or available to safeguard health information used for research purposes.

Another security measure that custodians and health record administrators should consider is excluding researchers from direct access to health records. If health facilities have sufficient personnel and computer services capability, the information required for purposes of the study can be gleaned by facility staff. A fee could be charged for this service commensurate with the costs and time involved.

This approach has the advantage of restricting access to known staff personnel. It also avoids the disruption caused by outside researchers using limited office space and equipment. Adopting such a policy is a matter that must be determined by individual facilities and custodians. This is a policy matter that should be discussed at the level of senior administration and perhaps the board before changes are made.

ROLE OF THE HEALTH RECORD ADMINISTRATOR

The health record administrator is often overlooked or underestimated as a key component and an important official when conducting human research. When a project involves health information research, it is the health record administrator who must develop a mechanism for access to the information. The health record administrator carries considerable responsibility in this regard in view of the ethical and legal consequences for unauthorized use or disclosure of health information.

RESEARCH ENTRIES IN HEALTH RECORDS

Research subjects are often drawn from the population of a health agency or provider where they are receiving established clinical treatment. Due to factors such as a particular illness, age, sex or livelihood, these individuals may be ideal subjects for research projects. However, caution must be exercised in the information that is entered into individual health records to avoid confusion between clinical treatment and research protocols. Research protocols may be combined with treatment records and contain medication orders and treatment regimes.

Health facilities or custodians should establish clear-cut policies and procedures for research entries. This may mean that research notations are made and stored separate and distinct from routine clinical documentation, are made on a colour-coded chart that denotes a combination of treatment and research, or complied in a style of writing for specifically created research entries.

Drawing a distinction between research and routine treatment notations is important for ensuring care of the individual, integrity of the research project and audit and reimbursement mechanisms. The chief concern is to maintain quality care. Entries in the clinical record that are confusing or irrelevant to ongoing treatment may jeopardize an individual's health.

Routine tests and daily observations may or may not affect the outcome of a study. However, the failure to distinguish treatment from research could cast doubt upon the findings of a research project. This could happen in a drug study, for example where a person suffers an adverse reaction to a known clinical drug on the same day when a research drug is given. Improper documentation could lead to the conclusion that the new research drug was responsible for the reaction. A carefully drafted notation indicating when the person received both drugs, the time of the reaction, and the symptoms will all help to reduce the chance of reaching the wrong conclusion.

Difficulties could arise in financial auditing if it is subsequently determined that research drugs were included in the expenditures of health agencies. Research drugs are usually covered by research project funds and should not be a cost to the health agency. With the current schemes for insurance coverage, it may be difficult or impractical to separate one from the other. However, with ever-increasing restraints on health expenditures, this may be one area in which belt-tightening may require careful entries to distinguish clinical drug treatment from research protocols.

DOCUMENTATION OF CONSENT

One type of entry that is important for human research is documentation of consent. This may be in the form of a written consent form or a detailed note or both. The format is largely a matter of preference for the health agency, the ethics review committee and the funding agency. The Tri-Council Policy Statement should also be taken into consideration.

Some jurisdictions have legislative requirements that must be met for any consent, including a consent for disclosure of health information for research. For example the *Health Information Act* in Alberta requires an express written consent as follows:

> 34(2) A consent referred to in subsection (1) must be provided in writing or electronically and must include
> (a) an authorization for the custodian to disclose the health information specified in the consent,
> (b) the purpose for which the health information may be disclosed;
> (c) the identity of the person to whom the health information may be disclosed;
> (d) an acknowledgment that the individual providing the consent has been made aware of the reasons why the health information is needed and the risks and benefits to the individual of consenting or refusing to consent,
> (e) the date the consent is effective and the date, if any, on which the consent expires, and

(f)   a statement that the consent may be revoked at any time by the individual providing it.[42]

Any specific legislative requirements of the jurisdiction or the particular health care sector must be satisfied.

In addition to the above, the process of consent and the documentation of consent for research purposes should include the following considerations:

- a clear description of the subject of the consent in question, as consent may be required for different activities such as for participation in the research, for disclosure of health information or for being contacted by the researcher for additional information;
- a description of the research project including a description of randomized trials and placebos if involved in the research project;
- for biomedical procedures an explanation of the research or experimental nature of the project including the procedures that are not generally recognized or accepted along with any therapeutic services furnished to the subject;
- an explanation of the alternative procedures that might be advantageous for individuals in the situation of the subject;
- the responsibilities of the subject including time, cost, reimbursement for expenses, compensation for injury and duration of the project;
- an explanation that a decision not to participate in the project will in no way negatively affect the quality of care provided and a description of the care that will be provided even if the subject decides not to participate;
- an assurance that the subject will immediately be given any new information that is relevant to the decision to continue or withdraw from the research;
- an explanation of the confidentiality and privacy for the individual undertaken by the research investigator including who will have access to information collected and steps that will be taken to protect privacy;
- how the research will be published and how subjects will be informed of the research results; and
- name and telephone number of a contact person in the event that the research subject has any questions during the study and a contact or resources outside the research team for possible ethical issues that arise during the research.

---

[42]   *Supra*, n. 7, s. 34(2).

The research documentation should state that the subject's consent to participate and consent to disclosure of health information is to be given freely without undue influence or coercion. Further, it should indicate that the subject was both legally and mentally capable of agreeing to participate in the study.

Some health agencies are incorporating a clause into research forms to address the possibility of commercial use of tissue removed during a study. This is the result of a case in which the Supreme Court of California ruled that a man was entitled to know that tissues removed from his body for purposes of treating his leukemia were of great commercial value.[43] In other words, the individual should have had the opportunity for an informed choice regarding whether or not he wanted his tissues used in that manner.

In that case,[44] the tissues were worth millions of dollars after they became commercially viable. Such a clause in a research consent document might be worded similar to:

> The research subject agrees that any tissues, body fluids or bone removed from him/her during the course of the study which is or has the potential of being marketed commercially is considered the property of the principal investigator with no residual rights in the research subject.

This terminology may not be understood by the research subject. A much more straightforward approach such as the following is warranted:

> If during the research project it is learned that tissues or fluids removed from you can be developed commercially, the researcher reserves the right to do so for his/her own gain or that of the health care agency.

Research subjects should be informed that they have the right to consent or refuse to participate in the study on this basis. They can insist on their share of actual or potential profits. However, researchers may not agree to participate on this basis and potential subjects may be lost from the study.

---

[43] *Moore v. Regents of the University of California*, 90 Daily Journal D.A.R. 8010 1990, affg. 249 Cal. Rptr. 494 (Cal. Ct. App. 1988).

[44] *Ibid.*

FOREIGN HUMAN RESEARCH

Ethics review committees, custodians and health record administrators should familiarize themselves with foreign research requirements for private agencies and foreign governments when participating in such projects.[45] Pharmaceutical firms, medical device manufacturers, and private funding sources such as non-profit foundations may have their own criteria that must be met in a research protocol. The health agency or custodian must consider its own guidelines and those of the foreign group for purposes of research review and should adopt the higher standard.

Although the foreign criteria are used in addition to those ordinarily used by the ethics review committee, these additional requirements carry considerable weight. If the committee should fail to incorporate the foreign criteria in its evaluation, a project could be turned down for funding. In conducting this additional analysis the ethics review committee should be careful to review any health information restrictions or usage or disclosure requirements that may alter the design of the study. The failure to comply with foreign requirements could surface during an annual review by the outside funding source, jeopardizing continuation of the project.

PRACTICAL CONSIDERATIONS

The following is a list of considerations that should be addressed in the collection, use and disclosure of health information in human research:

- periodically review the agency policy for human research to ensure quality care for individuals receiving treatment while participating in research projects;
- ensure that the well-being of research subjects is the highest priority and that subjects are advised of any new information that might affect continued participation in the research project;
- periodically update all research policies, procedures including the research ethics approval process to ensure compliance with new research requirements including the Tri-Council Policy Statement, ethical standards and legislation;
- ensure that funding agency requirements are met in the design of the study as well as in the approval and conduct of the research project;

---

[45] See, for example, *Selected International Legal Norms on the Protection of Personal Information in Health Research, supra,* n. 1.

- implement procedural steps for documentation for research purposes including the retention, storage and disposal of research documents as well as details such as treatment entries and research notations;
- make provision for the process of consent and the documentation of informed consents for research projects;
- ensure that adequate safeguards exist for the protection of confidentiality, privacy and security of health information including details such as whether health information may be used or disclosed without identifiers to link data to individuals;
- ensure that clear guidelines exist for contacting individuals and families of index subjects for additional information or follow-up studies;
- develop a confidentiality pledge for staff and researchers to sign before starting a research project;
- develop a standard research agreement that covers expectations that must be met by researchers and that addresses transborder data flow (if applicable); and
- develop staff in-service and orientation programs to educate and keep staff current regarding research obligations.

17

Risk Management in
Health Information

INTRODUCTION

With continuing concern about liability, a number of steps have been
taken to minimize this risk and to improve the quality of health services.
These steps include stricter requirements for medical staff privileges,
staff responsibility, continuing education, utililization review, total quality management/continuous quality improvement (TQM/CQI) and risk
management. Designed to pinpoint actual or potential sources of harm to
individuals and their property, risk management may avoid or minimize
costly litigation and quasi-legal proceedings.

Even an unsuccessful lawsuit brought against a health facility or a
health professional can be expensive, even when insurance costs are born
by the malpractice insurer for a facility or by the Canadian Medical Protective Association for physicians. Non-monetary costs of damage to mo-
rale and to reputation may last for years regardless of how unjustified
the allegations may be. The staff time and resources required to investi-
gate, discuss and respond to suggestions of malpractice can have a detrimental effect on the individuals involved and on the ability to provide
quality care.

The risk of litigation can be controlled, though never removed. It is essential therefore, that every provider of health services, whether it is a
research teaching hospital, an outpatient physiotherapy clinic, or a solo
medical or dental practice, have a comprehensive program to identify
and manage liability risks. Increasing requirements to conduct risk management activities and demands from the public for accountability of
health facilities and providers are evident in public inquires such as the
Dubin Inquiry for the Toronto Hospital for Sick Children and the more
recent inquiry involving pediatric cardiac surgery in Manitoba.

A key element in a risk management program is the documentation
used to identify and resolve problems of quality and potential risk and

injury.[1] This chapter includes a discussion of risk and quality management techniques along with the documentation required and whether risk management documents are protected from disclosure.

RISK MANAGEMENT: AN OVERVIEW

In any comprehensive risk management program, there are at least five chief components. The system is usually administered by a "risk manager", although in some health care agencies the responsibility for managing the program may be given to a committee or an assistant administrator. In larger agencies a combination of committee and risk management personnel may also be employed. In medical, dental or other professional practices, the system will not be as complex, but someone must be designated to be in charge — even if it is the practitioner alone.

A smooth-functioning risk management program requires support from the administration. It also requires assistance from the managers and directors of all departments. Risk management is an unrelenting process that, if successful, will curtail cost and loss from personal injuries and property loss or damage.

RISK MANAGEMENT TECHNIQUES

Although the five steps discussed below are usually found in risk management programs, other measures may be added to accommodate the needs of individual health facilities. More sophisticated data retrieval methods may also generate information that goes beyond injury prevention and incorporate cost-saving steps.

---

[1]   J.H. Haydon, "Legal Aspects of Health Information" in *Health Law in Canada*, Vol. 20, No. 2, November 1999, 1, at 8.

Figure 1
Schematic of Health Care Risk Management

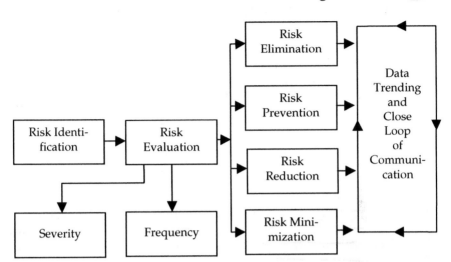

1. *Identify.* The first step in risk management is to identify both actual and potential sources of harm to individuals or their property. This can be done on an *ad hoc* basis as incidents occur or retrospectively by assessing health information and tissue pathology and safety committee reports, assuming these are relevant.

The identification of risks is not a task restricted to administrative personnel. Reports of injury to individuals, residents or clients or to their property may be made by physicians, nurses, dietary personnel and others. However, for retrospective analyses of incidents data collection may be facilitated by health record personnel.

2. *Evaluate.* The second step in a risk management system is to evaluate actual and potential risks in terms of severity and frequency of occurrence. Having such information in hand assists in determining which areas of the operation should be given priority. The evaluation process may also point out areas of duplication in services and expenditures that can be curtailed.

3. *Eliminate or Reduce.* The next step is to take action on those risks that can be eliminated. Some risks can be alleviated by taking a common sense approach to safety. Equipment that is faulty or out-of-date should be removed from use. Environments that are unsafe for patients, residents, clients, staff or visitors should be corrected, such as crowded hallways, slippery washroom floors, turned up carpets, insecure or nonexistent railings, furnishings that can fall over such as bookcases or lamps, and doors leading to unexpected stairways. Elimination of risks requires a review of past injury episodes to identify areas of potential

harm in the future. New opportunities for injury should also be identified and eliminated as part of an on-going program.

A risk management system may also uncover risks that cannot be eliminated but may be reduced in frequency and severity. In this part of the program, it is important to identify the types of potentially injury-producing activity that falls into this category and to set priorities for dealing with the problem. Reducible risks may involve individuals who are poor candidates for complicated surgery or people who suffer severe allergic reactions to contrast dyes in diagnostic tests. Better health care histories and preparation for quick remedial action may lead to fewer injuries or less undesirable outcomes.

4. *Prevent.* Next, take preventive measures. This includes regular review and planned maintenance of equipment and review of all administrative procedures. Considerable emphasis must be placed on constant education and re-education of personnel at all levels. This training includes instruction and reminders on the risk management program as well as safety information and effective communication skills. New staff should be introduced to standardized record keeping and language formats throughout the health facility or agency as well as protocols for treatment of individuals or residents injured while on the premises. Policies relating to damaged or lost personal property of individuals should also be explained.

5. *Minimize.* The last type of action found in most risk management programs is risk minimization. It is comparable to the safety restraint used by window cleaners or safety nets used by high wire circus performers. These actions decrease the risk where other mechanisms for preventing or controlling risk are insufficient.

A policy and procedure manual may specify that a crash cart is to be in the outpatient department. Having it fully stocked, updated and ready to use when a person experiences an adverse reaction to a dental anaesthetic may be the main factor that prevents an undesirable outcome from escalating into an anaesthetic death. Having the cart in place and the right people trained and in attendance to use the equipment is equally important. Without these measures, the policy and procedure requirements are nothing more than a paper exercise.

In some health facilities other techniques may be added to a comprehensive risk management program. However, the basic ingredients remain the same: identification, evaluation, elimination, reduction, prevention and minimization of risks. With a historical perspective on past injury to persons and property and risk of potential injury, a health agency can take steps to combat future problems. All of this information requires paperwork. Good quality data demands accurate and competent recording.

6. *Monitor.* Regardless of what sort of program is established, it is absolutely vital that the program be constantly monitored to ensure that it is being carried out, that it is appropriate to the changing conditions, and that it is effective. Having an outsider review the program at regular intervals or at times when the style or nature of the practice has changed can provide the most effective manner in which a monitoring can take place.

RISK MANAGEMENT INFORMATION SOURCES

There are a variety of information sources for identifying both actual and potential sources of risk including:

• incident reports	• medication error reports
• security occurrence reports	• property loss or damage reports
• malpractice insurance claims	• property loss claims
• workers' compensation reports	• occupational health & safety reports
• utilization management reports	• medical credentialing
• environmental rounds	• word of mouth information
• unanticipated returns (hospital or O.R.)	• inadequate consents
• research event reports	• discharges against medical advice
• infection control reports	• adverse drug reports
• drug profiles	• performance appraisals
• P & T Committee reports	• morbidity and mortality reports
• autopsy reports	• labour-management reports
• letters of complaint	• fatality & public inquiry findings
• grievances	• exit interviews

• staff turn over	• satisfaction surveys (patients & staff)
• decisions of professional regulatory bodies	• decisions of labour tribunals
• breaches of privacy	• access complaints
• threat risk assessments	• privacy impact assessments

There are also many risk identifiers available for situations other than facility settings. For example, in offices, medi-clinics and home care the information sources include missed appointments, homemakers denied entry, and allegations of theft from the client or family members. Health agencies and providers have considerable risk information available in the health record and through quality improvement and audit activities. Chart reviews and audits can be done retrospectively or concurrently for high risk situations or individuals. Different identification methods can be combined to develop a better understanding of risk factors.

An important risk identifier is pre-treatment risk screening. Before individuals undergo surgery, before a client is accepted for home care or long term care, careful screening should be done to determine both actual and potential risk factors. Once evaluated, appropriate decisions can be made whether to perform surgery at the health facility or whether to accept the client for long term or home health care.

Most health care agencies do not utilize the vast array of risk identifiers readily at their disposal. Instead, they place undue emphasis on occurrence or incident reporting. Resources are focused on designing forms, teaching staff how to complete the forms, and determining who is authorized to see the information.

Because the information could be used against a staff member or a colleague, many individuals are reluctant to complete incident reports for fear of "fingering" a friend or receiving a negative performance appraisal. Others recognize that reports can trigger a series of events where they may become witnesses in internal administrative or external legal proceedings. These concerns create reluctance to complete incident reports.

The net effect may be skewed and inaccurate data, and misleading trend analysis. The limited resources of the risk management program could be used ineffectively. Depending upon the definition of a reportable incident, many reports may describe low risk events and serious events may not be reported. Focusing only on incident reports could mean that serious risks are "missed" as a result of staff reporting behaviour or the incident reporting system.

Sophisticated risk managers do not place undue reliance on the incident reporting system. They use all practical means of identifying actual and potential sources of loss. Risk managers have moved away from the traditional incident report with its emphasis on the "after-the-fact" approach to risk identification to the so-called "Observable Events" reports. (See Figure 2.) The idea is to encourage staff to report factors, trends or observations, which provide very early warning of potential risk. This coverage is far broader than traditional incident reporting systems.

Figure 2
The Scope of Risk Detected Is Greater With Observable Events Reporting Than Traditional Incident Reporting

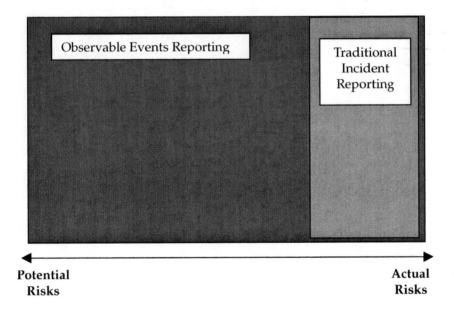

| Observable Events Reporting | Traditional Incident Reporting |

Potential
Risks

Actual
Risks

QUALITY MANAGEMENT

Quality management includes risk management activities. It is a broad term than can be used to encompass traditional quality assurance activities, utilization management and TQM/CQI. Quality management generates a considerable amount of paper for administrative purposes. The goal is to improve the quality of health care and to deliver it in as cost effective a manner as possible. Health information is used and reused in an effort to identify weaknesses and strengths and to maximize benefits in the health delivery system.

Quality management reports, committee reports, paretto charts, fishbone charts, storyboards, flow charts, control charts and a host of other forms and diagrams are used in various approaches to quality management. Like other documentation, the failure to use the information in a consistent manner can come back to haunt a health agency, particularly where it can be shown that the information put the agency "on notice" of substandard care and remedial steps were not taken. If it can be demonstrated that reasonably foreseeable harm was likely to ensue for example from an outbreak of nosocomial infections, the ground work would be in place for negligence litigation.

An effective approach requires managing the documentation in quality management activities. A rational approach should be followed in deciding what is and what is not essential information. Clear cut policies should be in place, which address the following issues:

1. Who has access to quality management information?
2. What is recorded in quality management documents?
3. How long should quality management reports be retained and in what format?
4. How does the risk management process relate to quality management and exchange information?

By addressing these and related questions, a clearer picture will develop for carrying out quality management activities.

DISCLOSURE OF RISK AND QUALITY MANAGEMENT INFORMATION

The disclosure of risk and quality management documents is a contentious issue. Individuals are now routinely exercising the right of access to their personal and health information. Legal counsel representing injured patients as plaintiffs seek to compel facilities to disclose incident and quality management reports either pursuant to client consent or under provincial rules of court in litigation. Health professional bodies now require members to demonstrate ongoing professional competence and quality.

Most provinces have FOIP legislation in force that creates a statutory right of access for individuals to their own personal information. Some provinces now have health information legislation that creates a specific right of access for individuals to access their own health information. The right of individuals to access their own personal and health information was discussed in more detail in Chapter 7 — Access to Health Information.

Where individually identifiable personal or health information is contained in risk and quality management reports, those documents are responsive to access requests. However, health information contained in risk and quality management reports may fall under exceptions to disclosure. For example, under the *Health Information Act* in Alberta:

> 11(2) A custodian must refuse to disclose health information to an applicant
>
> ...
>
> (b) if the health information sets out procedures or contains results of an investigation, a discipline proceeding, a practice review or an inspection relating to a health services provider, or
>
> ...
>
> (d) if the disclosure is prohibited by another enactment of Alberta.[2]

The Information and Privacy Commissioner in Alberta has issued an Order upholding a custodian's duty not to provide access to practice review information compiled in response to a complaint about a surgeon.[3]

Similarly, the *Personal Health Information Act*[4] in Manitoba precludes a trustee from giving access to information compiled for quality assurance and risk management or precluded by another enactment. Specifically, the Manitoba Act does not allow trustees to give individual access to health information about peer review by health professionals, review by a standards committee established to study or evaluate health care practice, bodies with statutory responsibility for discipline of health professionals or for purposes of risk management assessment.[5]

A similar access provision exists in the *Health Information Protection Act*[6] that is enacted but not yet proclaimed in Saskatchewan. The draft Ontario legislation precludes individuals from a right of access to health information involving quality of care information, quality assurance program information under the *Health Professions Procedural Code* or under the *Regulated Health Professions Act*.[7] The draft Ontario legislation contemplates a separate act for quality of care information in the *Quality of Care Information Protection Act, 2002*.

---

2 R.S.A. 2000, c. H-5, s. 11(2)(b) and (d).
3 Order H2002-002, Calgary Health Region, Alberta, May 2, 2002.
4 S.M. 1997, c. 51 (C.C.S.M. c. P33.5).
5 *Ibid.*, s. 11(1)(d).
6 S.S. 1999, c. H-0.021, s. 38(1)(d).
7 *Ontario Draft Privacy of Personal Information Act, 2002*, s. 58(1)(a) – (c), released February 2002 as a consultation on the draft.

Although incident reports may be relevant and admissible as evidence (refer to Chapter 6 — Health Information as Evidence), a more common question is whether such documents can be compelled by individuals or by plaintiff's counsel before trial. Ordinarily incident reports are not considered privileged documents. During the so-called "discovery" phase of a lawsuit, solicitors for both sides obtain both documentary and physical evidence. At times a plaintiff or a defendant will seek to block discovery on the ground that the information sought is privileged.

There are different types of privilege that could apply to risk management documents. Privilege refers to the special legal rule where witnesses and documents are exempted from answering questions or producing documents during legal proceedings.[8] Privilege is a narrow exception to the usual duty to provide all relevant information to other parties in legal proceedings and to the court. Privilege may arise under common law court decisions or by legislation.[9] Common law privilege may arise under the Wigmore criteria or in the form of solicitor-client privilege or litigation privilege.

The health record is a relevant and producible document when the quality of care is at issue in litigation. There is debate whether incident reports are part of the health record, as the report is usually prepared as a result of an unexpected or undesirable occurrence that arises during the provision of health services. The practices of facilities vary for storage of incident reports and other risk management documents.

Some facilities store incident reports as part of the health record while other facilities store these types of documents in a separate place for administrative purposes. Most hospital and long term care legislation across Canada does not list incident reports as a part of the health record.[10] However, there are exceptions such as the *Nursing Home Operation Regulation* in Alberta, which lists unusual occurrence reports as part of the resident record.[11]

Common law privilege is determined on a case-by-case basis. Canadian courts apply a test called the Wigmore criteria[12] to determine whether privilege exists. There are four criteria that must be met for the court to determine that privilege exists. The evidence must show that: the communications originate in a confidence that they will not be disclosed; confidentiality must be essential to the relationship; the relation-

---

[8] N.J. Inions, *Privilege and Quality Assurance: The Issues for Canadian Hospitals* (Ottawa: Canadian Hospital Association Press, 1990), at 61; Canadian Nurses Protective Society, "Privilege" InfoLaw 2000, at 1.

[9] J.H. Haydon, *supra*, n. 1, at 6.

[10] *Ibid.*, see *e.g.*, *Public Hospitals Act*, R.S.O. 1990, c. P.40.

[11] *Nursing Homes Operation Regulation*, Alta. Reg. 258/85, s. 11(1)(i)-(iii).

[12] J. Wigmore, *Evidence in Trials at Common Law*, revised by J. T. McNaughton, vol. 8 (Boston: Little, Brown, 1961), at para. 2285.

ship ought to be fostered; and the injury that would arise to the relationship by disclosure must be greater than the benefit gained for the correct disposal of litigation.[13]

The Wigmore criteria have been argued and determined in cases involving psychologists and therapists, hospital committee records for physician credentials and privileges and in a nursing audit committee report.[14] The Wigmore criteria are unlikely to be satisfied for incident reports that are generated on a routine basis for internal administration and communication purposes.

Solicitor-client privilege arises when a client seeks legal advice and prepares a document for a solicitor in contemplation of litigation. Since incident reports are usually written in the ordinary course of business and long before litigation is anticipated, a claim of solicitor-privilege would usually be unsuccessful. For a claim of solicitor-client privilege to be successful it must be shown that a document was prepared for the purpose of providing the report to the solicitor.

Solicitor-client privilege is not absolute and can be set aside for overriding interests such as for public safety. For example, in *Smith v. Jones*[15] the opinion in a psychiatrist's report that was prepared at the request of the accused's lawyer, was ordered to be disclosed to protect other victims from imminent danger. Even where privilege exists, privilege may be lost where privileged information is given to individuals outside the privileged relationship.[16] A claim of solicitor-client privilege might be sustainable in rare circumstances where incident reports are prepared specifically for legal counsel in serious incidents.

Another type of privilege that arises at common law is litigation privilege. Litigation privilege arises where a document comes into existence for the dominant purpose of litigation.[17] For example, reports obtained from witnesses to an incident that resulted in a personal injury suit would be privileged from disclosure when prepared to defend the litigation. However, if an internal document such as an incident report was prepared only secondarily for litigation the document would not be privileged.[18]

---

[13] *Ibid.*

[14] E. Picard and G.B. Robertson, *Legal Liability of Doctors and Hospitals in Canada*, 3rd ed., (Toronto: Carswell Legal Publications 1996), at 413.

[15] [1999] 1 S.C.R. 455.

[16] *Re YBM Magnex International Inc.* (October 15, 1999), Doc. No. Calgary 9801-16691, Paperny J. (Alta. Q.B.).

[17] *Shaw v. Roemer* (1979), 38 N.S.R. (2d) 657, 69 A.P.R. 657, 12 C.P.C. 152, 11 C.C.L.T. 35 (T.D.).

[18] *Ibid.*, see also *Christie v. Royal Insurance Co. of Canada* (1981), 17 Man. R. (2d) 200, 22 C.P.C. 258 (Q.B.).

Courts have found that statements given to insurance adjusters before litigation was contemplated are not privileged.[19] The dominant or main purpose of incident reporting is usually for administrative purposes, to avert and identify possible litigation and to prevent future harm to individuals and property. Incident reports are not usually be protected by privilege under the dominant purpose test. However, the existence of this type of privilege depends upon the circumstances.

Protection and privilege for risk and quality assurance documents can also arise in legislation. Some provinces have passed legislation that protects certain records from discovery in legal proceedings.[20] The Newfoundland and Labrador provincial *Evidence Act* provides a strong case for arguing that incident reports are privileged documents.[21]

The *Alberta Evidence Act* creates a statutory privilege for quality assurance committees and documents.[22] This Act says that a witness cannot be asked or permitted to answer questions about proceedings before a quality assurance committee. Similarly a witness cannot be asked to produce or permitted to provide a quality assurance record in a legal action.

In the *Alberta Evidence Act* a "quality assurance activity" is defined as:

> 9(1)(a) "quality assurance activity" means a planned or systematic activity the purpose of which is to study, assess or evaluate the provision of health services with a view to the continual improvement of
>   (i)   the quality of health care or health services, or
>   (ii) the level of skill, knowledge and competence of health service providers,[23]

A "quality assurance record" is defined as a record of information in any form that is created or received by or for a quality assurance committee in the course of or for the purpose of its carrying out quality assurance activites.[24]

The *Alberta Evidence Act* describes a "quality assurance committee" as a body with the primary purpose of carrying out quality assurance activities.[25] The quality assurance committee could be appointed by a regional health authority, provincial board, hospital board, operator of a

---

[19] *General Accident Assurance Co. v. Chrusz* (1999), 45 O.R. (3d) 321 (C.A.).

[20] *Evidence Act*, R.S.B.C. 1996, c. 124, s. 57; *Manitoba Evidence Act*, R.S.M. 1987, c. E150 (C.C.S.M., c. E150), s. 9; *Evidence Act*, R.S.N.B. 1973, c. E-11, s. 43.4; *Evidence Act*, R.S.N.W.T. 1988, c. E-8, s. 13; *Evidence Act*, R.S.N.S. 1989, c. 154, s. 60; *Medical Act*, R.S.P.E.I. 1998, c. E-8, s. 52; *Saskatchewan Evidence Act*, R.S.S. 1978, c. S-16, s. 35.1.

[21] *Evidence Act*, R.S.N.L. 1990, c. E-16, s. 6.1.

[22] *Alberta Evidence Act*, R.S.A. 2000, c. A-18, s. 9. This provision was introduced as the *Quality Assurance Activity Statutes Amendment Act, 1999* and came into force with Royal Assent on April 29, 1999, repealing the previous s. 9.

[23] *Ibid.*, s. 9(1)(a).

[24] *Ibid.*, s. 9(1)(c).

[25] *Ibid.*, s. 9(1)(b).

nursing home or established by an enactment or designated by an order of the Alberta Minister of Health and Wellness.[26] There may be different points of view as to whether a quality assurance activity includes a risk management activity and documents such as incident reports. However, this legislation provides a strong basis for this argument.

Determining the existence of privilege may be compounded by the arsenal of charts, graphs, and storyboards used in TQM/CQI. Recent changes to the evidence acts often speak in terms of "quality assurance" rather than "quality management". Claims that TQM/CQI forms and quality management documents fall under the protection afforded by the amended laws has the potential to engender a new set of challenges requiring interpretation of evidence legislation.

Protection of quality and risk management documents from disclosure may also arise under other types of legislation. For example the *Health Information Act* in Alberta allows a custodian to disclose health information without consent to a committee that has the primary purpose of carrying out quality assurance activities as defined in the *Alberta Evidence Act*.[27] However, a quality assurance committee must not disclose this information to any other person and may only disclose the information to another quality assurance committee in non-identifying form.[28] Restrictions on disclosure of health information compiled for quality of care purposes also exists in the *Health Information Protection Act*[29] in Saskatchewan.

Changes in legislation governing the health professions foreshadow change for quality assurance and quality management reports. The *Regulated Health Professions Act, 1991* in Ontario is a good illustration,[30] which requires regulated health professionals to demonstrate quality assurance to their respective professional colleges.

The *Health Professions Procedural Code*[31] in Ontario requires the council of each college of a health profession to establish a Quality Assurance Committee to determine whether members have committed an act of professional misconduct, are incompetent or incapacitated. The Ontario legislation establishes protection from disclosure as these records are not admissible in civil proceedings.[32] A similar provision exists in the *Health Professions Act* in Alberta, which authorizes limited disclosure.[33]

---

[26] *Ibid.*, s. 9(1)(b)(i)-(iii).
[27] *Supra*, n. 2, s. 35(1)(g).
[28] *Ibid.*, s. 35(2)-(3).
[29] *Supra*, n. 6, s. 27(4)(h).
[30] S.O. 1991, c. 18, ss. 80-83.
[31] Schedule 2 of the *Regulated Health Professions Act, 1991*.
[32] *Regulated Health Professions Act, 1991, supra*, n. 30, s. 36(3).
[33] R.S.A. 2000, c. H-7, s. 52.

Health agency based reports and health information will be used for purposes not contemplated a few years ago. An incident report or quality management document prepared for purposes of improving care may actually be used for regulatory or disciplinary purposes and vice versa. These issues are not usually considered along with evidentiary privilege.

It should also be pointed out that resorting to legal fictions will not prevent an incident report from being subject to discovery. Writing across the report or stamping "For Solicitor Only" will not create privilege under existing case law.[34] The courts will look beyond the facade of a claim of solicitor-client privilege and determine whether or not the dominant purpose test is satisfied in the circumstances and whether the incident report is producible.

Unless the legislation specifically creates privilege for quality and risk management documents, legal counsel defending health agencies may have difficulty persuading a judge that incident reports come within the protected umbrella of privilege. The situation in each jurisdiction must be carefully considered.

Those concerned about the discoverability of incident reports say the information contained therein may damage or prejudice the defence of the health agency or provider. They also argue that knowing a document may be discoverable will result in personnel being less candid. Neither contention is insurmountable in a well-functioning risk management program.

If written in a concise and objective fashion, incident reports should not pose a serious threat to the defence of litigation. Many other pieces of evidence must be brought together to determine legal liability. The incident report may or may not play an important part in the health agency defence or the allegations of the plaintiff. Much depends upon the circumstances of each case. It should be remembered that liability may be established without an incident report. Seen in this light the discoverability of incident reports should not be of overwhelming concern.

The point cannot be reiterated strongly enough: worrying about the application of protective legislation is not as important as developing good reporting systems and utilizing the information properly. The plaintiff's bar is increasingly sophisticated. Legal counsel representing plaintiffs are no longer satisfied with summary discharge sheets. Plaintiff's counsel wants all relevant documents and information to effectively represent their client. Unless laws are in place to clearly establish privilege, plaintiff's counsel will probably get the desired information.

---

[34]   *Taylor v. Lailey* (1959), 27 W.W.R. 257, 17 D.L.R. (2d) 738 (Man. Co. Ct.).

PRACTICAL CONSIDERATIONS

Whether a health organization is a tertiary care hospital, a long-term care facility, a home care agency, a clinic or the office of a solo practitioner, the reality of today's practice requires a system to control, manage and minimize the risks of liability, and to manage the quality of the care given. In each situation the system is somewhat different in its complexity and sophistication. However, the basic practical principles of operation are the same. The principle is that the organization must make a management decision that it will establish a risk management system and will incorporate it into its daily administration.

The following steps are recommended.

1. *Set up a regularly scheduled risk management review.* This review should take place on regularly pre-determined dates. This may be every three months, or every six months or what ever length of time is practical. The interval should not however, be too long.

The purpose of the review will be to determine whether there are new risks, which have arisen, whether the past risks are still present, and whether the actions being taken to manage those risks have been effective.

It is important that such a review be set up on a regular basis. The danger in not following this practice is that it will only take place when someone happens to think of it.

2. *Conduct a risk management review at any time when the conditions or the risks have changed or when there is any indication that a risk has materialized.* The question that must be asked is whether the system is working and if not, why not.

3. *Examine each of the areas involving health information in which a risk of liability could arise* (see Figure 3). If the health information system is seen as a chain, it becomes obvious that risks may arise at any link in that chain. It is therefore important to determine whether the management of the risks is effective not only in the overall health information system but at each link in that system.

Figure 3
Sources of Liability Risks

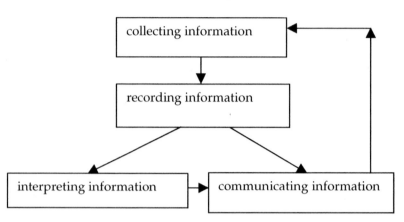

4.　*Develop an assessment form to be used in the risk management review.* This will provide a checklist so that no item will be forgotten, and will provide a means of comparison among departments, and among the various assessments done over time.

5.　*Appoint a specific person to be in charge of risk management.* In large institutions, there is usually a full-time risk manager or someone with that responsibility. In smaller organizations, this task may be the responsibility of someone who has additional responsibilities. Even in a small medical, dental or other office, someone must have the responsibility over risk management including the risk management of the health information system. Failure to have a designated individual frequently results in no one taking the responsibility, and does not allow anyone person to build the experience and expertise in risk management.

6.　*Coordinate the risk management efforts regarding health information with risk management programs on other matters such as medical staff privileges.* The risk of liability frequently arises from a combination of factors in a number of different activities including health information. This requires the collection of risk management information from a number of sources within the organization, comparing them with the information collected about the health information section, and analyzing the findings together.

7.　*Collect information not only on potential risks but on actual incidents that have occurred and actual claims.* Analyze how each occurred and whether it arose from a failure in the health information system.

8.　*Educate staff.* There must be a continuing program to educate all professional, technical and administrative staff on the importance of risk management generally, and particularly with respect to health information. The education program must include an understanding of the risks involved and the requirements needed to manage those risks. It must have as its goals a change in attitude toward the risks involved in health information, and a change in behaviour so that all staff follow the requirements necessary to manage those risks and maintain the necessary quality. The attitude that health information processes are merely a formality has no place in any health organization. The education program must be constantly changing in response to the risks discovered in the risk management assessment.

9. *Establish procedures and policies specifically designed to avoid or minimize the risks of liability.* (See Chapter 18) These procedures and policies should be kept under regular review as a result of risks arising throughout the health industry, and as a result of risks that are particularly of concern when the risks assessment is performed.

10. *Establish a method of enforcement.* If possible a method must be devised to ensure that all staff comply with procedures and policies, and to management risks. Simply identifying risks, adopting policies and procedures to deal with them, and then doing nothing about those individuals who refuse to comply, places those individuals and the organization at risk.

11. *Monitor the results of risk management efforts for compliance and for results.* Failure to monitor may result in efforts that are misdirected or useless.

18

Prototype Policies and Procedures

The risk of lawsuits and other legal actions arising from health information issues can never be totally eliminated. Hopefully, these types of risks can be reduced, although it is difficult to estimate the magnitude of the risk. In some instances the risk has never materialized or has never given rise to a reported court decision. In determining a solution to any legal risk, one has to balance the risk against the practicalities. The solution may jeopardize the goal of the facility to provide quality care. In consultation with legal counsel, the facility must determine how far it is prepared to go in minimizing a legal risk and accepting it.

In drafting administrative rules or guidelines for minimizing legal risks, the rules must be custom-made to suit the health care organization or provider in question. The rules that are suitable for a general hospital may not be totally adequate for information maintained by a group medical practice or a home health care agency. In order to draft rules that are practical it is advisable to seek the advice of staff representatives from the various disciplines using or affected by health information.

Far too many entries are made in ignorance of this principle. As a result the communication of information about a person's condition or treatment is either not made at all, or it is made incorrectly. The person is injured or does not receive proper care and a claim for compensation or a subsequent lawsuit results. Only a continuing, persistent and effective in-house education program will overcome this risk, coupled with the auditing of information standards and enforcement of those standards.

The following provide basic guidelines for drafting policies and procedures for any health care agency or facility. These are prototypes and should be used only as a basis for drafting. Adaptations must be made to suit individual situations and organizations.

POLICY #1

RECORDING HEALTH INFORMATION

1. *Write legibly.* Poor handwriting results in important information being ignored or misinterpreted. In either case, errors in diagnosis, care or treatment may result, individuals may be injured and lawsuits take place.[1] (See also POLICY #2.)

2. *Write accurately.* Errors in orders, drug dosages and symptoms may not always be caught by the person taking action on the basis of recorded information. Injuries may result which may lead to claims for compensation. Accuracy is not only limited to the absence of errors. It also requires clarity and absence of ambiguity. The writing style handwriting must be easy to read and must eliminate any opportunity to misinterpret the information. (See Chapter 4 — Standards for Health Information.)

3. *Record concisely.* Only information that is essential should be recorded. Information should not be repeated within the same entry. Verbose writing may result in misunderstandings, the ignoring of essential information and, as a result, errors in care. Quick access to vital information may be impossible or difficult, thus resulting in injury.

4. *Record events chronologically.* Entries in the record should be made in chronological sequence. Some information systems are divided into sections, such as medical orders and physiotherapy. Within each section, the entries should be made chronologically. Failure to do this raises the suspicion that entries were made after a lawsuit was commenced or after an error was made in order to cover it up. It also raises the suspicion that if the chronological order is not accurate, the content may also not be accurate. In either case the credibility of the record is placed in doubt and the value of it as a defence tool in a lawsuit is decreased.

5. *Record information immediately or as soon as possible.* The failure to make an immediate record of an event can have two consequences. Both jeopardize the effectiveness of the information as a defence tool. Under many provincial evidence acts information can be entered into court as evidence of an event only if documented at the time the

---

[1]   Legibility is a serious issue. The Saskatchewan College of Physicians and Surgeons considers the matter so important that it has passed a by-law on the topic.

event occurred. A delay may result in the record being inadmissible or given little weight in court.

The second consequence may occur after the information is admitted. It raises two suspicions. The first is that the entry is not accurate and therefore cannot be believed. The person who made the entry may have forgotten between the occurrence of the event and the recording of it. The second suspicion is that the person who made the entry may not have made it in the course of the usual routine but to cover up for a wrongful act, which did not become immediately apparent. In either case the value of the information is diminished.

6. *Do not rush.* Whether recording information by hand or on a keyboard, it is extremely important that entries are not rushed. This is frequently the source of errors that are not picked up resulting in patient injuries and lawsuits.

7. *Read the entry immediately after making it.* Make certain that it states exactly what was intended, that it is accurate and that it is easily read and understandable to someone who may be in a different discipline and in a different organization or system. This applies to both handwritten and to keyboard entries.

8. *Do not assume that those who will be reading the handwritten information are familiar with the handwriting.* This is especially true in large organizations, and with the movement of information among personnel who are not familiar with other individuals.

9. *Do not assume that every person reading the information is familiar with the subject matter.* It is often assumed for example, that a physician or nurse working with a particular specialty will know what information, diagnosis, or medication or treatment is appropriate in certain circumstances. With information going to other disciplines, or other departments, and with inexperienced personnel being used in areas with which they are not familiar, absolute accuracy is required in all written communication and information.

10. *Do not assume that you can always read your own handwriting with accuracy.* With a large volume of cases, those who record information by hand will not necessarily be able to accurately read their own handwriting and will not necessarily remember the details of that which they wish to record.

11. *All entries in the record must be made by the person who was directly involved in the event recorded.* A nurse, for example, should not make an entry on behalf of another nurse. The nurse making the entry would not be able to testify as to the truth of the information she recorded if that nurse was not involved in the event or treatment. This does not prevent one person writing up the notes for another as long as the person involved in the event signs the entry. In that case, the person writing up the notes is not identified and would not be called upon

as a witness. This allows a stenographer to type up surgical notes that are adopted and signed by someone was actually involved in the events recorded.

There are also personnel who do not make entries in the record but who report what they did or saw to someone else who makes the entry. The entry in such a case should not say that a particular task was fulfilled since the recorder of the information really does not know whether it was completed. What can be entered is the name of the person who reported that a task had been done. No one should make an entry without being able to swear under oath that the information recorded is true.

12. *All entries must be signed.* Any signature should be immediately identifiable. The purpose of this rule is to aid in the communication process and to prevent misunderstandings, which can cause errors. If the person reading the entry wishes to make contact with the person who made it, the name of the person must be immediately apparent. If the signature is not clear, the name should also be printed. The use of self-inking stamps bearing a facsimile of the caregivers signature should be discouraged.

The clear identification of those having made entries is also required in the case of a lawsuit. Some of those who made entries may be required as witnesses. The inability of legal counsel to call the correct witness may clearly damage the defence of a case.

13. *The person who made the entry must sign all entries.* Failure to follow this practice can result in the same sort of delays and confusion as if the entries were not identified at all. Patients, nursing home residents, and home care clients may be injured and lawsuits may result. In the lawsuit itself, finding witnesses and being able to use them becomes difficult if not impossible, thereby damaging the defence.

14. *Write in ink.* No entries in the record should be made in pencil, as pencil recordings are too easy to erase without leaving a trace. The suspicion can be raised in the course of a lawsuit that the entry was altered to reflect more favourably on the defendant's position. While some inks can also be erased, the erasure is not usually as simple or as clean and thus the suspicion is not raised. Even if the suspicion is unfounded the very fact that it is raised damages the credibility of the party relying on it. Similarly, pens using inks that will run or smear should be avoided in order to avoid ambiguity. Where carbon copies are being made, soft felt tip pens should not be used. The copies must be clear and easily read.

15. *Try not to change pens in the midst of writing an entry in the record.* In the making of any particular entry the ink should remain the same. Otherwise suspicion may be raised when the record is presented in court that additional notes were added in order to cover up or to

augment the entry. This could seriously damage the credibility of the record and the defence. If pens are changed, that fact should be noted in the record.

16. *Use uniform terminology throughout the facility.* Failure to use the same terminology within a department or facility can cause breakdown in communication, especially when a person is transferred or even moved temporarily from one department to another. Injury and lawsuits may result. Uniform terminology within the health system is also desirable when communications flow among various organizations or providers.

17. *Use uniform abbreviations throughout the facility.* While nothing in law prevents the use of abbreviations of health information either in a record or in communications, it should be discouraged. The danger of the reader not understanding an abbreviation or misreading it is always present. However, if abbreviations are to be permitted they should be uniform throughout the organization. A list of mandatory abbreviations should be established and distributed to all staff who make entries or who make use of recorded health information.

    Organizations and individuals that regularly exchange information should also use uniform abbreviations. Information that goes to another health provider should, if at all possible, avoid the use of abbreviations, or at least in brackets have the meaning follow the abbreviation.

    New staff and others who make entries in or use the record must be instructed in the abbreviation system of the agency. Special care in the use of abbreviations can minimize the risk of communication errors and patient injury. It can also reduce confusion during a trial over the meaning of a record, which has been entered as evidence.

18. *Establish a uniform system of handwriting numerals.* The method of writing numerals must be the same throughout the organization or system. Everyone should make a "7" in the same way, so that it does not look like a truncated "4" or a "1", or a "9". A "5" should never be able to be interpreted as a "6". Nor should a "4" ever be mistaken for a "9". Nor should a "6" ever appear to anyone as a "0".

    There must be a standard system of making a decimal point, so that it never appears as a small 0, or as a 1.

19. *Encourage the use of handwritten block letters rather than cursive.* While this may not totally eliminate errors of interpretation, it may reduce the risk. It should at least encourage each letter being separate and not be confused with other letters. It should also avoid the problem of a small "r" being split into looking like a small "v". A cursive "c" may look like an "e", and an extended "I" without a clear dot may look like a small "t" without a cross. Individual letters may not cause

difficulties, but a combination of misinterpreted letters may result in patient injury or death.

20. *Use a uniform system of recording information throughout the organization.* It is not enough for the language to be uniform. The style of recording must also be consistent. For example, if nurses ordinarily record certain facts, the failure of one nurse to record that type of event on a particular occasion allows the judge to assume that it did not occur. The person attempting to convince the judge that it in fact did occur would have to present evidence to counterbalance the judge's assumption to the contrary. This new evidence may have to be in the form of oral testimony of a witness.

   The court is then faced with the testimony of a witness whose memory may be less than perfect. Statements that a particular event occurred or that a particular action was taken may not be credible. On the other side, the court is faced with a record written at the time which makes no mention of the event, even though such events are ordinarily recorded. It may be difficult to convince the court that it occurred through a witness who faced with a lawsuit may have much to gain by taking this position.

21. *Correct errors openly and honestly.* Errors are made in the written recording of information. Human error is an accepted part of any activity and usually will not be held against the person making the error unless the errors amount to negligence and cause reasonably foreseeable injury. The danger is that someone may attempt to hide the error. The discovery of such an attempt throws into doubt the truthfulness of the entire record. Can the court believe anything that is in the health record?

   It may also be important to be able to compare the original entry with the corrected version. This may assist staff in dealing with problems caused by actions based on the incorrect entry.

   It should be noted that the errors being discussed are not errors in information, which were believed correct at the time. Rather, these are errors which are discovered as a result of further investigation. The problem is that of errors made in the transcribing of information. To correct these errors openly and honestly use the following procedure.

   (1)   Cross out the entry to be deleted in such a manner that it is clearly deleted but can be read if necessary.
   (2)   Indicate by an arrow or other means where the corrected entry may be found.
   (3)   Record the date and time at which the correction was made.
   (4)   Sign and complete the correction in the same way.

(5)   Do not use a felt pen or white-out to obliterate the incorrect entry.

(6)   Do not cover the incorrect entry with tape and write the new entry on the tape.

(7)   Do not tear out the page on which the incorrect entry is written.

22. *Do not add editorial comments.* Entries to the health information must be strictly clinical, for the purpose of facilitating care and treatment. No comments are to be added reflecting on the character of any other person who has made an entry nor on the entry itself, nor on the person who is the subject of the entry, except in a professional manner. If findings disagree with those recorded elsewhere in the record, that fact must be stated without any reflection on the previous personnel. Comments reflecting the writer's opinion rather than a fact must be stated as an opinion.

Particular attention must be paid to entries indicating possible diagnoses, which, if discovered, could jeopardize a person's employment. If a condition is suspected the record should clearly indicate that it is suspected or being investigated. The record should not leave the reader with the impression that the individual in fact suffers from the disorder in question. Similarly, if a definitive diagnosis has not or cannot be made, this must be clearly indicated in the record. The principle of confidentiality alone must not be relied on to protect the individual.

POLICY #2

ACCESS TO HEALTH INFORMATION[2]

1. *Obtain the identity of everyone who wants access to health information regardless of who they are.* Every agency should establish a reasonable process for authentication of recipients of health information. It should not always be assumed that the person seeking access is who he or she appears to be. A white coat with a name tag may not be the doctor named on the tag. It could be an insurance investigator, a reporter or private detective. If the person is from outside the institution, their name and particulars should be recorded along with the date and time of their request.

---

[2]   See Chapter 7.

2. *Determine why the person seeking access to the information requires it.* It may be quite obvious in the case of those who are directly involved in the treatment and care of the individual. In the case of other health care workers or third parties from outside the agency it may not be.

3. *Make certain that the person seeking access to the health information is entitled to it.* A court order or subpoena and a written consent by the subject of the record or that person's guardian is sufficient authority. The fact that a person is a physician, nurse, police officer or lawyer does not carry with it authority to gain access to a record. From an organizational point of view, it is often easier to ensure confidentiality of records if only designated personnel are authorized to give access. There should always be someone available to advise staff as to who may or may not be allowed access to a record.

    Particular attention should be paid to researchers who have not necessarily been authorized.

4. *Establish a policy and procedure for patients to have access to their own health information.* Such a policy will avoid confusion as staff and information move from department to department. No policy should be established without advice of legal counsel to make certain that it conforms to existing legislation. This policy must be updated at any time that legislation changes. It is absolutely vital that all personnel are fully aware of the policy and procedure and are able to implement it. It is also important that patients and their families are made aware of it.

POLICY #3

OPERATION OF A HEALTH INFORMATION SYSTEM

1. *Read health information in context.* Professionals in various disciplines may frequently read health information in light of their own discipline without taking into consideration the context in which the information arises. This may result in incorrect diagnoses or treatment, and patient injury. All staff must be educated to do this. Patients and families who have access to health information must be carefully instructed as to the context in which information is found. Failure to do this may result in inappropriate and even dangerous decisions regarding treatment. Such decisions by lay persons may be considered as negligence on the part of physicians or other health professionals.

2. *Do not discuss a patient's health information in public.* Nothing about a patient, resident or client must be discussed in public places such as elevators, cafeterias, lounges or in front of any person who is not entitled to have access to that information, including other staff members, patients, or family.

3. *Do not display a patient's health information in public.* Apart from informational signs such as "Nothing by mouth" posted above or near a patient's bed, nothing that indicates the patient's condition should be posted or left in any place where those who are not involved in the care and treatment of the patient might have access to it.

4. *Develop a policy on destruction of records.* A precise procedure must be developed to prevent access to records and health information that is to be destroyed, and a method of destruction devised and implemented.

5. *The retention period of records shall be based on a uniform policy.* Because of the legal implications of record retention, microfilming and destruction, a policy shall be established for the entire organization following the advice of legal counsel. If any particular department requires an exception, this decision shall be made in conjunction with the overall policy. Failure to follow this practice may result in decisions that ignore provincial retention requirements and evidence requirements. (See Chapter 5 — Retention, Storage and Disposal.)

6. *The method of destroying records shall be based on a uniform policy.* The destruction of some records and not others, the method of destruction and the procedure of microfilming followed by destruction are all issues that must be determined by one policy throughout the organization. The policy must be based on legal advice, on evidence legislation and relevant health legislation. The policy must also concern itself with problems of confidentiality regarding proper disposal of records. (See Chapter 10 — Faxes and Health Information.)

7. *The record system must be designed in such a manner that warnings will clearly stand out.* Because of the serious risk of injury due to drug and food allergies, drug interactions and activities incompatible with the person's condition, caution or warning signals on the record must be clearly visible to anyone who looks at the record. The failure to draw these problems to the attention of the reader creates a serious liability risk and risk of patient injury. It may also may create a risk to staff and visitors if the patient is a risk to others.

8. *The record must be designed in such a way as to prevent the loss or removal of pages.* Many health information records are simply a clip board or a loose file allowing for the loss or removal of material. This may result in injury from actions being taken without the benefit of the missing information. It may also damage credibility in a lawsuit.

9. *Establish a uniform policy on student entries.* Throughout the agency a uniform policy should be established relating to the following matters:

   (1) whether medical, nursing and other students are to make entries into the records;

   (2) if students are making entries as to whether there are to be any restrictions on them;

   (3) whether student entries are to be countersigned and who is authorized to countersign;

   (4) as to how the entry is to be identified as having been made by a student; and

   (5) whether student entries are to be segregated from the main body of the record.

   The purpose of such a policy is to ensure that special attention is taken regarding care that may not be equal to that given by the experienced professional. This extra attention will assist in overcoming the shortfalls in standards, which may otherwise cause injuries and lawsuits.

10. *A policy must be established with respect to entry codes and personal identifiers on computerized records.* (See Chapter 8 — Confidentiality, Privacy and Disclosure to Third Parties, and Chapter 9 — Computerization and Information Linkage.) Such a policy is to include:

    (1) limited access to individual and staff identifiers in order to maintain confidentiality;

    (2) limited access as to who can make entries and as to who can make changes;

    (3) establishment of a system that supplies documentation that is acceptable in local courts as evidence. Due to the uncertainties in the law with respect to the computerization of records, special care is necessary to avoid problems. A strict policy throughout the institution based on the advice of legal counsel will assist in this task.

11. *Establish a system for modifying or correcting records.* (See Chapter 9 — Computerization and Information Linkage. Also refer to Chapter 7 — Access to Health Information.) Make certain that the original entry is not changed, and that provision is made to show what is now the correct entry. (See POLICY #1, sec. 17, governing hard copy record corrections for guidance.)

12. *Establish a protocol for reverting back to hard copy charting when computer systems fail.* Make certain staff know how to maintain continuity of care when a computer record system crashes.

13. *Establish a protocol on the use of faxed communications.* (See Chapter 10 — Faxes and Health Information.) Make certain that staff know how to use faxed communications, taking into account record confidentiality, a secure location for the machine, copying thermal paper, retention of fax documents, secure lines and verifying that the appropriate party is contacted prior to transmission.

14. *Establish a protocol governing risk and quality management documentation.* (See Chapter 17 — Risk Management in Health Information.) Make certain that records of risk management and quality management activities are properly secured and used.

15. *Establish a protocol for disseminating information to third parties, such as the media and police.* (See Chapter 8 — Confidentiality, Privacy and Disclosure to Third Parties.) Make certain that the issue of consent is addressed as well as the limits of disclosure, for example, in emergencies for locating someone who has eloped.

16. *Establish a policy on computerized information and Smartcards.* (See Chapter 9 — Computerization and Information Linkage.) Make certain that procedures, which include assuring that the information is accurate and current and that adequate privacy and security protections exist, for using Smartcards are in place.

Appendix

THE USE OF PROTOTYPE FORMS

The forms in this section are to be used as illustrations only and as reference in the drafting of forms. Provincial legislation or government directives may require forms drafted in a particular manner. In addition, forms must be drafted to suit the needs of the individual health facility or provider. Furthermore, regardless of the contents of the form, the failure to administer the form correctly may invalidate it as evidence in the defence of a lawsuit.

Therefore, it is vital that the person signing the form is mentally capable of doing so. The person must understand the meaning of the form and what legal rights are being given up in signing it.

The person must also have the legal capacity to sign. The right to sign must not have been taken away either by legislation or by a court order. If a person is signing on someone else's behalf, he or she must have the legal authority to do so.

In either of these situations, there should be documentary evidence.

FORM #1

CONSENT TO TREATMENT

I, _____ of _____
consent to the performance of _____ (name of procedure)
by _____ M.D. (name of doctor) and such other persons selected to assist.

The purpose, nature and probable risks and benefits of this procedure
have been explained to me by my attending physician,
Dr._____. The risks of this procedure include
_____, _____ and _____ . The
hoped for benefits include _____, _____
and _____

I further understand that the purpose of this procedure is to (brief description)

_____

I have been advised of the reasonable alternative procedures available
to me, and I have declined such alternatives. These alternatives include
_____ and _____ . I have been informed of the
probable risks and benefits of these alternatives.

I understand that I am free to refuse this procedure and that I have
been informed of the probable risks of refusal.

I have been given the opportunity to ask questions regarding this procedure, and that any questions I have asked have been answered to my
satisfaction.

I accept that in all medical and surgical procedures there are risks that
cannot be anticipated, and that no guarantees have been given to me as
to the outcome of this procedure.

I have made my decision freely, without undue influence or coercion.

_____
(name of patient)

_____

(signature of patient)

_____

(witness)

_____

(date)

Note: Despite the signing of this form, plaintiffs can always allege that despite the form, they were not told of certain risks. Patients are never in a position to know whether they were told everything or not. They only know what they were told, not what they were not told. It is therefore advisable for the doctor who informed the patient, preferably the doctor who is to do the procedure, to sign an additional statement.

I, _____ M.D. have informed the above _____ of the information referred to, and that in my opinion he/she was mentally capable of understanding the information given.

_____

M.D. (signature of physician)

_____

(date)

Note: If the patient or a person consenting on behalf of the patient has been given information about the procedure in written form, or via a film or video, the form should include an acknowledgement that this material has been read or seen. Specific reference to the title and other identifying features should be included. Form #2

FORM #2

PERMISSION TO TAKE PHOTOGRAPHS OF PATIENT

I, _____, give my consent for the taking of photographs of _____ (area of body to be photographed) by _____ (name of photographer). I understand that these photographs will be used by the _____ (name of health facility) for the purpose of study and medical research, and that no information which might reveal my personal identity shall be used.

I also understand that these photographs will not be reprinted, published or otherwise reproduced in any scientific or academic journal or book or any other publication, or other means of reproduction without my further written authorization.

_____
(patient's name)

_____
(patient's signature)

_____
(witness)

_____
(date)

FORM #3

RESEARCHER'S PLEDGE OF CONFIDENTIALITY

I understand that as a member of the research staff investigating various pharmaceutical agents in the treatment of venereal diseases, I shall maintain strict confidentiality of information involving the use of research subjects' records and any information, including the identity of the subjects.

I agree not to disclose or discuss such information unless specifically authorized to do so by my superiors.

I understand that a failure to abide by this requirement could cause individual subjects embarrassment, and that it could have consequences for the subject with family, friends and associates. I appreciate that an unauthorized disclosure could have consequences for the subject in regard to employment.

I also acknowledge that as part of my employment relationship if I should make an unauthorized disclosure of research subject information I may be dismissed from my position as _____. I appreciate that I shall be legally responsible for my actions, and in the event of litigation for unauthorized disclosure of information, I agree to indemnify my employer for any damages incurred.

_____
(researcher's/employee's name)

_____
(researcher's/employee's signature)

_____
(witness)

_____
(date)

FORM #4

PATIENT'S PROPERTY RELEASE

I, _____ of _____, assume all responsibility for all property brought with me or for my use to the _____ Hospital while I am a patient in the said hospital.

The property referred to includes clothing, jewelry, money, toilet articles and any other personal possessions.

I hereby release the _____ Hospital, its medical staff, and all employees and volunteers for the loss of, or damage to, any of the said articles regardless of the cause of such loss or damage.

Signature of patient: _____

Date:_____

Signature and name of witness _____

Note: A detailed list of property with a signed acknowledgement may be attached to the form. If this procedure is followed, reference should be made to this list in this form. Both should be dated.

FORM #5

TEMPORARY ABSENCE FROM HOSPITAL

I am temporarily leaving the _____ (name of health facility) with the permission of my attending physician, _____ M.D. I shall leave the facility at _____ (AM) (PM) on _____ (date), and return on _____ by no later than 8:00 P.M.

I understand that the hospital assumes no responsibility for any personal property that I leave in the institution during my absence that I have not surrendered to the business office for purposes of safe-keeping.

I also understand that the hospital shall not be held responsible for any harm that may occur to me during my absence.

_____

(patient's name)

_____

(patient's signature)

_____

(witness)

_____

(date)

FORM #6

PATIENT LEAVING HEALTH FACILITY
AGAINST MEDICAL ADVICE

I, _____, of _____ (address) have decided to leave the _____ (name of hospital) against the medical advice of my attending physician, _____ M.D. I have made this decision freely, without duress or coercion.

I have been informed of the possible risks and dangers to my health arising from my leaving the health facility at this point in my hospitalization.

I understand that the health facility, its employees, and my attending physician will not be held responsible for any harm to me arising from my leaving the hospital.

_____
(patient's name)

_____
(patient's signature)

_____
(witness)

_____
(date)

I, _____ M.D. am the attending physician of _____ whom I have advised not to leave the _____ (name of hospital) and whom I have advised of the potential risks in so doing.

_____
(signature of physician)

_____
(date)

FORM #7

CONSENT TO THE RELEASE OF INFORMATION

I, _____ of _____
authorize (check those as are appropriate):

(a)   Dr._____

(b)   the staff of the _____ Hospital

(c)   the staff of the _____ Clinic

(d)   the administrator of _____

(e)   the Social Services Department of the _____Hospital

to release any information contained in my record held by _____
for the purpose of referral to the following agencies or institutions or individuals:

_____

_____

_____

_____
(signature)

_____
(signature and name of witness)

_____
(date)

FORM #8

The form on the following page is illustrative of a contemporary screening tool used in health care risk management to document the emergency exception to the requirements for consent to treatment. It also provides health care professionals with an opportunity to identify patients with underlying medical conditions and those with particular needs or treatment requests.

Sample Form to be Adapted to Local Law and Conditions

Emergency Department Screening Tool	Patient Addressograph Information

Caregiver: ——————— Position: ————————————

Time: ——————————— Date: ————————————————

Check-off All Appropriate Boxes

(1) *Description of Patient Condition Requiring Treatment Without Consent*

☐ Unconscious

☐ Under Apparent Influence of Drugs Unable to Participate in Consent

☐ Under Apparent Influence of Alcohol Unable to Participate in Consent

☐ Severe Pain Unable to Participate in Consent

☐ Apparent Underlying Mental Disability Unable to Participate in Consent

☐ Life-threatening Emergency Requiring Immediate Attention

☐ Health-threatening Emergency Requiring Immediate Attention

☐ Urgency of the Situation Prevented Contacting Others Who Could Authorize Care

(2) Patient Arrived with the Following:

☐ Medic Alert Cards
☐ Medic Alert Medallions
☐ Organ Donor Cards
☐ Armband or Bracelet Restricting Treatment
☐ Advance Directives
☐ Health Care Proxy
☐ Durable Power of Attorney in Health Care
☐ Living Will
☐ Form Restricting Treatment on Religious Basis
☐ Funeral Instructions
☐ Other (Describe) ———————————
———————————————————————

Describe Documentation in Box (3)

■ Describe Life-threatening Emergency: ————
———————————————————————

■ Describe Health-threatening Emergency: ————
———————————————————————

(3)   *Information Found on Patient Documentation:*

☐ DNR ——————————————————————————————
☐ Allergic to: ——————————————————————————
☐ Sensitive to: ——————————————————————————
☐ Asthmatic Taking: ———————————————————————
☐ Diabetic Taking: ————————————————————————
☐ Heart Disease Patient on: ————————————————————
☐ Implant Device or Prosthesis: ———————————————————
☐ Requests No Blood or Blood By-products ——————————————
☐ Other (Describe) ———————————————————————
———————————————————————————————————

[Consent Policy & Procedure Reference No.]
[Hospital Form Reference No.]

Index